THE
SAGE
TRAIN

THE
SAGE
TRAIN

PHILOSOPHY COMES TO LIFE

NICKY HANSELL

Occasional graphic content in the context of ethical issues

Matador
9 Priory Business Park
Kibworth Beauchamp
Leicestershire LE8 0RX, UK
Tel: (+44) 116 279 2299
Email: books@troubador.co.uk
Web: www.troubador.co.uk/matador

ISBN 978 1784623 463

British Library Cataloguing in Publication Data.
A catalogue record for this book is available from the British Library.

Typeset in Garamond by Troubador Publishing Ltd

Matador is an imprint of Troubador Publishing Ltd

For Iona, Peter and Patrick
and in memory of my much loved father,
Edward Clement Blower

I would like to thank the very many people who have helped me with this work and suffered the manuscript in its various guises. Tim Clissold, Jonathan Clack, Chris Rycroft, Karen Maters, Beatrijs Brouwer, Jerry Twomey, Margaret Gibson, Dan Short, Joe Jenkins, Jim McCormack, Peter Morris and Moray Welsh have all been more than brilliant – thank you. Students over the years have been a source of deep joy – thank you for your enthusiasm. My brothers, Robert and Tony Blower, who have in very different ways been so important to the telling of these stories and the underlying quest on which we are embarked. Thank you to my dear husband, Roger, who never fails to see the heart of the matter and to my children Iona, Peter and Patrick who are each extraordinary and who light up my life. But my greatest thanks must be reserved for my mother, Adeline Blower, in whose presence many of these tales were written, and whose wisdom has been my constant guide.

Nicky Hansell, Aug 2015

Aquinas in his study
Beatrijs Brouwer

PREFACE

Philosophy reaches far into our lives. We use it every day and often don't realise that what matters to us and why it matters is meat and drink to philosophy. It is the stuff of gossip, intrigue, opinion and belief. When we say 'Well he did it for the greater good,' we are echoing the philosophy of John Stuart Mill. And when we say, 'To hell with it! I'm going out tonight and I don't care what happens!' we're going right back to a little known Greek called Aristippus who put personal pleasure before everything else. Philosophers are literally lovers of wisdom and whenever we question any of our actions we are all, in some way, philosophers.

I wrote this book to explore a new way of unpicking philosophy. My students always liked the little details best; the fact that Spinoza was a lens grinder or that Aristotle was buried next to his wife. Once they could imagine the man, it made the step to understanding his meaning seem shorter. Although the events are fictitious, the characters are based more or less on what we know of these men (and historically it is, nearly always, men) and the lives they lived.

I have always admired the great liberal, John Stuart Mill who did so much to change the lot of women, possibly had an affair with the married Harriet Taylor and was broken hearted when she died. His particular brand of utilitarianism grew to be miles away from the more quantifiable version of his mentor, Jeremy Bentham. Mill's 'greatest good for the greatest number' was not measured by statistics but by the colour and value of the happiness it gained. But that happiness (whatever it is) is a legitimate goal, and that what happens as a result of our actions matters more than the action itself, is absolutely central to this fierce Victorian. His polar opposite, Immanuel Kant, disregarded consequences altogether. For Kant, duty and sticking to the rules is what marks someone out as 'good'. It is better to be tempted and to resist than not to be tempted at all. Kant's supreme stature in the philosophical world is unquestionable. In real life, Kant's devoted servant was a man called Martin Lampe and it was he, not Josef Steigler, who followed his master's daily walk. It doesn't matter. Josef is in many ways different to Martin but shares with him a sense of the precise order of the breakfast table and Kant's unstoppable routine.

The philosophy is painted with a broad brush stroke, with my apologies for everything I have simplified in an attempt to make it accessible. Wherever possible, I have used biographical information to construct a tale that reveals something of the man and his theory. So Hobbes really was afraid of spirits and slept with his servant for protection and Aquinas was a tall, quietly spoken Dominican who, towards the end of his life, had a profound mystical experience. He was a towering intellect and a humble man and for the sense and flavour of him I drew on the biography by GK Chesterton himself.

Chesterton and Nietzsche were an unlikely pairing. Nietzsche had famously gone mad towards the end of his life and although his philosophy was in many ways anathema to the Catholic author of the Father Brown mysteries, there was also an uneasy admiration. Nietzsche had trouble with food while on earth, so I thought he should be hungry in heaven, while Chesterton's huge corporeal frame housed a man who embraced life and literature with fierce optimism. He was, in the words of George Bernard Shaw, a man of 'colossal genius' and I have always loved him, from first reading his stories in school.

These tales are about people who made profound and unique contributions, not only to the lives we live but to our whole internal landscapes. Our reverence for science has some of its roots in Aristotle, our love of the abstract in Plato. Hobbes, Aristippus, Aristotle, Ayer, Mill, Spinoza, Aquinas and Kant were not randomly selected. I could have included others, but the fact is that these were the men who spoke to me and in whom there remains huge richness. They were wise as well as being clever. I am all too aware that if they were to read these tales themselves, they would throw up their hands at the simplicity of the rendition – or, I hope, they might just chuckle.

What 'good' might be; how we find it, and what it means is something many of us are interested in – and these Sages were interested too. Along the way they also came up with ideas about God, language, freedom and love without which we would be meaner. Socrates' famous words that 'the unexamined life is not worth living' summed up his beliefs at his trial. Mill said virtually the same thing two and half thousand years later. The Sages have left us their 'examination tools'; a wealth of different perspectives with which to continue the journey.

Nicky Hansell

The Sage Train

The mountain path twisted and turned, first one way and then the other, but the man didn't pause or deflect from his walking. He just strode on like one possessed. He was dressed in nineteenth-century garb with walking socks and a coarse woollen jacket, designed to repel the worst of the weather but mostly unequal to the job. And the weather was changeable.

He walked to the right of the mountain, ascending steadily and catching sight of the snowfields on the great flank above him. To his right, the slope fell sharply so that when his foot dislodged a stone, it rolled just a little before tumbling into the void and falling to the rocks a mile or so below.

The man paused to catch breath and survey the scene beneath him. He could see the path in the distance that he had climbed first thing that morning. The trail meandered away, so he followed it, reliving in his mind's eye each step of his journey. There was the tarmac and the thundering juggernauts; there was the well by the road and the girl who had pulled up her bucket, undressed and poured water all over her body when she believed she was all alone. 'Woman', he had tried to say, 'I can see you quite clearly', but apparently, she could not see him. So he had sat and watched her bathe in astonishment, finding her beautiful when he had expected only revulsion. And it was then that he'd realised he was dead.

He didn't know how long he had been in this state, though he suspected it was a very long time. It was not unpleasant, though he yearned for someone to talk to because so many things were so strange. These lorries, for example, that swallowed up the valley roads and the speeding cars that passed them. And the way the people talked – speaking into pads held up to their ears or into the air itself. He didn't understand the people.

He sighed and pressed on. Though he had no idea where he was going, he knew that he had to get there, and that this "life", if such you could call it, was a journey. It was the one thing beyond his control. He was also aware, dimly but with increasing certainty, that the mountain path that twisted to the distant snow plains above him was his creation and choice.

He was just thinking there was no one interesting in Heaven, when he saw someone ahead on the path. He made a mental note that one of them would have to step aside as the approaching figure was very large, but then he realised how unusual it was! Someone, or something, was coming down from the mountain. Nietzsche quickened his step. He was going to stop and talk! In all his traipsing, this was the very first man to be going in the opposite direction.

Studying him as the other approached, he saw a sort of giant. Six foot at least with a girth like a walrus, and a tweed cloak wrapped round his shoulders. On his head there was a hat, tilted in a slightly absurd way. Indeed there was something absurd about the fellow in general, but the philosopher took this as a good sign.

'Good day!' he called out, as the huge man approached. 'What a wonderful view! Is it even clearer further on ahead?' He wondered if he should be so trite. Would a 'Moral Hero' really be interested in the landscape?

The man made as if to pass by and Nietzsche found himself making the bold and embarrassing decision to reveal that he was vulnerable.

'I went mad you know! Stuck in silence for eleven years with my brain gone to mush in my head. It's a pleasure to meet a man like you. After my own heart, I mean.'

'Mad?' enquired the giant, laughingly.

'No, no. Brave and unique. For you're the only person I've met going down.'

'Up or down – what matters? But if you are the madman, Nietzsche, you will forgive me if I pass you by. I have no patience with drivel!'

Nietzsche squared his shoulders. He was used to rejection and pain. Had he not driven himself mad out of love for the rejecting world? Anyway, that was how he saw it. But there was something in the great man's good humour that galled him. Made him shrivel up and small. Why was he cast out? He had only destroyed the old myths. Surely, this Hero had no truck with myth!

The man swept past, his cloak flapping in the breeze as he whistled and breathed in the air. 'Wonderful!' he muttered, 'Quite wonderful!' and he laughed at nothing at all.

He was not four foot down the path when Nietzsche called out again. 'Won't you stop and talk to me? I have not talked for years!'

'I can't talk to someone who can't laugh,' called the other, over his shoulder.

'But I can laugh. Look at me. I laugh like a child. Ha ha!'

'That's not laughter,' said Chesterton, open-mouthed. 'That wheeze you're making sounds more like a snake than a man! It has nothing to do with joy. Quite apart from that, I'm not sure I can talk to a person who claims to be God!'

3

'I didn't claim to be God. That was just a joke,' muttered the German, morosely.

'Not a very good one.'

'No, maybe not. But I can explain what I mean, if you would just give me some time.'

'Very well,' replied the giant, retracing his steps. 'If only because my moustache is better than yours and you look so horribly alone. Allow me to introduce myself – G K Chesterton, early 20th century, journalist and writer of tales.'

'Friedrich Nietzsche,' said the other quite pompously, then deflated himself and said, 'Just call me Fred.'

'Why – when you're not English?'

'What does it matter when we're both dead? Isn't nationality transcended by death!' Chesterton smiled at that, swept off his cloak and put it on a rocky outcrop so they both could sit down. He lit a pipe and puffed contentedly. They sat in a silence that was far from friendly and more on edge than relaxed.

'Look at that train of people,' said the philosopher, finally, remarking on a snaking phalanx winding its way ahead of them.

'Yes. An Age Chain.'

'A what?'

'An Age Chain. You know, people from different periods in history all strung together in one chain. They all have a common purpose. That one,' said Chesterton, wiping his glasses, 'That one appears to be looking for Truth. A sequence of philosophers who devoted their lives to the pursuit and knowledge of Truth. I suppose we could call it a Sage Train,' and he chuckled. 'Why aren't you on it? A great Philosopher like you? Weren't you concerned with Truth?'

'Only in that I said there was no such thing,' said the

German bitterly, scratching his moustache and looking crestfallen. He would have liked to have been in the illustrious company and not stuck on a rock with a fat man who might not be "The Übermensch" after all.

'And you weren't the first to say it! Many people contested Truth. That's the trouble with you Moderns. You think that the Ancients never thought of your ideas. Of course they thought of them. It's just that they didn't think very much of them! But look at them, all strung out like a procession of donkeys. Let's play a game and see if we can recognise them!'

'Very well,' said Nietzsche, uncomfortably. He had no doubt that he could play, but he was still smarting. He didn't like to be told that the people seen in the distance, like a column of wooden toys, could come anywhere near him in brilliance.

'I'll go first as I am a philosopher and you're not. Which one of them,' said Nietzsche, peering and straining his eyes, 'said you must practice Virtue like an archer? He's back into fashion just now, partly as a result of my work!'

'Old or young?' asked Chesterton. 'No, don't answer, that's easy. Aristotle of course; the seeker of purpose. You can see him there, walking with Plato, showing the way to the rest. Very well, my turn. Which one of those men bought Aristotle to Europe and made him acceptable to the Church?'

Nietzsche looked at him sharply, 'You know I don't like religion. Why would I look to the church?'

'No, no, my man,' Chesterton laughed loudly. 'You can't just select the people you like! Come on, which one of those great minds we can see in the distance, said that the purpose of a human life was to return to where it had started – into the arms of God?'

'Well, I know of course,' said Nietzsche, 'but I can hardly

bear to spit his name out, it is so disgusting. Aquinas! There, I've said it. Right I'm having two goes in one. Take your eye back a bit along the line and you see some stragglers talking together. I called one a "sickly invalid" and the other a "vulgar blockhead". Both descriptions are apt. God knows why they're talking so much – they had nothing in common in life. And the centuries kept them apart!'

The journalist twisted awkwardly and wished he'd not invented the game. 'Look here, my man! I'm not sure I can stomach such a slight on two of the greatest of minds. Perhaps you didn't understand Spinoza and you certainly misread Mr Mill. Why is he vulgar?'

'He's vulgar because he assumes that everyone is equal and has an equal right to happiness. It's a thought that makes me sick!'

'Makes you sick?' said Chesterton, getting out an enormous sandwich, carefully tied in waxed paper with string. 'How can another's happiness make you sick?'

'Because people aren't equal! Only the brave and the strong are admirable – only they should thrive and they should do so at the expense of the rest!'

Chesterton undid the wrapping, spread a silk 'kerchief on his knees and proceeded to munch contentedly.

'Don't you think you wrong yourself by saying that?' he asked, after a minute of chewing. 'I mean, to the unsympathetic ear that sounds like the thoughts of a madman – which I know you unfortunately were. But doesn't it occur to you that a Hitler might agree with your words?'

'Well, yes, that's the trouble. All right. I'll try and rephrase. For too long man has lived in awe of a system that no longer exists – the idea of God. In my age, with Darwin and so forth, everyone was anxious about God. They suspected Him of not being there. And if you take that seriously – really seriously – then you have to construct a new kind of morality. My attempt was to say that boldly.'

Chesterton concentrated, for the philosopher spoke with unusual passion. It seemed to exhaust him, however, for he sat looking crumpled and small.

'I propose we leave the subject,' the journalist muttered between bites, feeling a little guilty at raising the subject of madness. 'I can see we will never agree, and the Sage game is already boring.'

'Bah!' said the German unhappily, for the bread smelt fresh from the oven. The journalist had covered it with mustard, and the ham was glistening and moist.

Seeing his eyes and tasting his hunger, Chesterton rummaged around in his knapsack and pulled out another large parcel. He handed it to the philosopher who unwrapped it deliberately.

'Thank you!' he said, after the first bite. 'That is delicious. You didn't have to share it, my friend.'

'I have plenty more,' said the enormous Englishman, peering again in his sack. 'Enough to keep me going for a time. But better not be grateful. It's against your beliefs you know! In the realm of sandwiches, I am the stronger. In your world, there is no sharing. But there's something else down here. Strange – it was not here this morning.'

Nietzsche glanced over and sniffed contemptuously.

'Good heavens,' said the journalist pulling out a tattered old book, its pages all stuck together. 'This appears to be a collection of stories.'

'Hmmm,' said Nietzsche, ignoring him. 'This is good. *Verr gut!*' Secretly he was glad of the company and didn't want the big man to leave.

7

'Good heavens,' said the journalist again, laying his own sandwich on a rock to better study the book. 'Well I never! What a thing!'

'It is an old thing this rubbish,' said Nietzsche, munching contentedly as he glanced at the journalist. 'It is not of any use.'

Chesterton laid the book on his lap, looked up at the Sage train and down again at the book, appearing to do a tally.

'Well I never! I really never do!'

'What?' spat his companion.

'What an extraordinary thing! All those philosophers you see over there – they all have their tales in this book. There they are; Aquinas, Mill, Spinoza. Look they're all there!' He shoved the book in the direction of the philosopher who glanced at it without interest, a large piece of mustard clinging to his moustache.

'So?'

'Well don't you see? Here is this book and there are those men. Why don't we read all about them? Visit them in their homes so to speak. It has arrived in my sack for a reason.'

The German looked doubtful. 'I don't know if I want to read about them. I'm not concerned with what they wore, or which women they did or didn't love. All this is no interest to me.'

Chesterton was not to be put off. 'No, Teuton! You can't decide in advance what is or isn't interesting. How do you know till we've read it? My proposition is simple. We read the stories to visit the philosophers. Let them show us their ways.'

'Well that's no good,' grumbled Nietzsche. 'You can straight away see the flaw there! How do we trust these stories – they will be twisted and bended I know!'

It was Chesterton's turn to look disgruntled.

8

'If I knew you better, I would say that you are happy to destroy a perfectly good idea with nothing at all to replace it. Go on then, you think of a plan!'

Nietzsche finished the sandwich and allowed the unusual sense of a full stomach to work its way into his brain and the first glimmer of cheerfulness. 'Very well,' he said, finally. 'What if we read the book but don't tell the Sages?'

'Go on,' said the journalist, cautiously.

'So, wherever possible, we enter the story. Become part of the scene so to speak – from the sidelines,' he added hastily, seeing the journalist's face. 'Read of someone they had dealings with. Where the philosopher had an impact but was not the main player at all!'

'I can't see how you can alter the book. I wouldn't have thought that was possible. But very well. If that's the only way you're prepared to play. We read with no expectations and travel wherever it takes us?'

'No expectations,' said Nietzsche nodding excitedly. He was much happier like this.

'Are we going to bicker about who to read first?' said the journalist, still wary and studying the index.

'I think we should start at the beginning,' said Nietzsche, settling himself back and looking longingly at the knapsack. 'This obviously means Plato.'

'You mean Socrates.'

'No, Plato! The only possible place to start!'

'But that's absurd. In fact, I'll go so far as to say I won't read if we don't start with Socrates, the man who invented debate. There's no other place to start!' Chesterton was becoming heated and his face was growing red. 'Besides', he said, leafing furiously through the pages, 'I can't seem to find Plato here.'

'That is because you are not looking!' scowled his companion, grabbing the flimsy brown thing. 'There!' he said, jabbing with his finger, 'There is Plato! There he is! Chapter One.'

Chesterton grabbed the notebook back with a surprisingly agile movement. 'Not in my book!' he said triumphantly, holding the little thing up. 'Here it is quite clearly Socrates!'

'Nein,' cried Nietzsche. Excited at the smell of a battle, his eyes stared wildly and small flecks of spittle appeared on bits of moustache. 'We don't know what Socrates said! He never wrote anything down! Only Plato wrote for him. Of course he is not in the book!'

'Well I'm refusing to start with Plato,' said Chesterton, sulking. He didn't mind losing when he was wrong, but he objected when he was right. And he hated deferring to Nietzsche. They sat with their arms folded, glaring furiously as the Sage Train snaked its way upward and nearer to out of sight. The book lay docile and tattered.

'It's a stupid idea anyway,' said the German, finally.

'It's a ruddy good idea, you idiot little man. Very well. A compromise. We'll ignore both Plato and Socrates and start further on in the book. What do you say to that, Teuton? I'm going to turn to someone I admire, whom I know you dislike,' said the big man, quite cheerfully, picking it up from his knee.

'Very well then. I know who it will be. If there was another ham sandwich, I would have to let you win!'

'In pursuit of your few finer virtues, I'll pass you another. But then can we please sit back and let the stories unfold?'

'Verr gut,' said the philosopher again. Apparently it was his stock response to any and all types of food. They settled themselves more comfortably and attempted to focus their minds. The book lay open obligingly, set at a particular scene. Meanwhile, the wind which had been playing around them swept both men up like old-fashioned kites and instantly carried them high. She held them there, effortless and unmoving, hovering over the stories down in the valley below. It didn't matter that they could no longer see the Sage Train. She knew where each man had come from and exactly where each story was set. So she knew where to place them back down.

PARIS, MAY 1271

Thomas Aquinas

There were three children at the ford, barefooted and sailing twig boats down the stream. Their dusty faces denoted peasantry, while their playful eyes and ample grins spoke of a sufficiency in all the things a child needs most.

They had spotted the friar, or rather the friar's mule, making its slow descent down the winding path long before either the mule or the friar saw them, both being occupied with their own concerns. The mule was engrossed in picking out the easiest way between the white rocks, while the friar was immersed in the view beneath him and a sound closer to hand.

'I hear you, Brother Robin, I hear you,' he called to the bird, who had accompanied them all the way down the track, and who was just then eyeing them from the bough of an overhanging tree. 'I hear your song and I'm glad for it. Keep singing, little bird. God is in his Heaven, and all's right with the world.'

The mule stumbled on until the friar drew a halt and the animal rested, twitching its ears against the buzzing of the summer flies. Paris lay spread out beneath them and, in the distance, the growing wonder of Notre Dame Cathedral could easily be seen. The friar, Luc, stopped to catch breath, panting a little and sweat appearing below his hairline. He needed a rest but it was a good excuse to marvel at the distant wooden scaffolding where workers crawled like bees on honeycomb. From his vantage point the noise of construction floated up surprisingly clear. He could hear the shouts and exclamations, the rough word when a tool was dropped and the incessant chime of chisel against stone.

He roused himself, muttered encouragement to Sabine the mule, and continued his downward descent. He had spotted the children now, for they had run up to greet him, vying with one another as to who could reach him first.

'*Bonjour*, mes enfants. How are you all this beautiful day? How are you Uthièr? Did your knee heal itself with that ointment we put on?'

The child bent down to inspect the offending limb with an expression of the utmost seriousness before finally whispering, '*Oui*,' to the man in the brown woollen habit. He was shy, and it came out more as a whistle than anything else, but nothing could stop the dancing leap of his eyes.

'Then you have a very brave knee. And how is your mother, Morteau? Do you have a little playmate yet?'

Morteau nodded, hopping from one dirty leg to another. All three of the children giggled and held out their hands to beg.

'Away with you,' laughed Luc. 'Do you think I'm made of sweetmeats? Sabine has eaten all the good things.' But the children continued their dance, skipping unabashed, till he unfastened one of the leather panniers and drew out a cloth in which were wrapped five figs – purple, juicy and plump.

'*Tiens!* There you are.' Each child helped himself timidly before biting into the fruit with delight. Luc smiled as he watched them, then, noticing the mule, said, 'Do you see how she inspects us? What is it she wants to say?'

'She says she would like one too!' ventured Uthièr, with a crooked smile that revealed several missing teeth.

'Then she shall have one. And you shall be the one to give it to her. Take it like this; now… hold your hand flat.' The boy slunk back as the mule retracted her lips to reveal a mouth filled with more teeth than his own, but the friar held his hand and Sabine took the fig gently.

'There. Now she is saying, "Thank you kind Uthièr."' Luc helped himself to the last remaining fruit. 'She says she has a fine set of brothers who would share their figs with her. And, for reward, you will escort us over the river showing us the best place to cross, so my habit does not cling to my legs like a woman's wet robe!' The children giggled again and ran ahead, fathoming the water with sticks around either side of where they stood. 'This way, here! It is shallow. Here is the crossing!' Luc made a great play of picking his way delicately across the shingle, though in truth there was not much danger; the Seine tributary was low at this point, and the current not so strong that it could sweep any of them away.

He left the children to their games and made his way across the undulating landscape until he stood at the outskirts of the city by the southern gate, a narrow, cobbled affair, heavily populated at this time of day with people returning from the fields beyond the walls. It had been a long journey, and he was not sorry to feel the end of the dust and the buzz of civilisation as he led Sabine along the cobbles, ducking her through the alleys to steer the shortest route home. For once, it would be good to stop his wanderings and dine tonight at a table, instead of resting somewhere under a tree, wondering if he would be set upon or robbed. Old Aurensis, who shuffled rather than walked, greeted him at the gatehouse with a slap on the back and a prayer of thanks for his return.

'It's good to see you, Brother,' he said, clasping his hand and pumping it vigorously. 'Three weeks can go slowly when a friend is absent.'

'Ay,' said Luc, returning the greeting. 'Many a day's distance, but the mother house thrives and sends its regards.'

Before long, the mule was in the friary pasture tearing hungrily at the rich summer grass; her panniers removed, and the gold, which he'd collected from the main abbey, sent to the Prior who would know best how to use it. Luc permitted himself to sit for a while in the orchard and simply be. Although he could feel the city pressing in, clamouring and loud, he pushed it away. Let it wait, there in the background. The evening could wait. The return to his patients could wait. Only this mattered now; the call to love that was present in everything, from the click of the grasshopper to the peas climbing their pea-sticks. It was a love that enveloped and suffused him, emptied and filled him, renewed him every day in the gift of itself as mediated by creation. Just as he always did when he was true to himself, he wanted to stay in the love a while.

It was old Aurensis who roused him, not half an hour later, saying there was a carrier at the door with a wounded girl asking for him by name. Reluctantly, Luc got to his feet, said a brief blessing and prepared to go to the gatehouse. If he'd had power over time perhaps he would have held it there, frozen forever in a peaceful field where goodness and order lay carelessly around. He could not have known that his life was about to change and that evil was coming, striding down the streets to confront him.

* * *

15

If nothing else, the yellow hood of her trade would have marked her out as she pushed her way through the crowd. Face after face flared up before melting into the shadows. The faces started off distinctly; a pauper from the country, as lost and bemused as she, who stared at her in horror before hurrying on his way. Two ladies, their wimples white and well worked, pulling their hoods down and clutching at each other for safety. A young man astride a palfrey – this man hardly bothered to look, for he had seen it all before. It seemed strange to her that, despite everything, all she could think of was the burning need to urinate. She took herself to the side of the street trying to press herself into obscurity, and lifted her tunic. Almost immediately the warm gush of liquid puddled around her feet, splashing into the filthy hides that were all she had for shoes. The thought that in ancient times Egyptian women stood to urinate while the men squatted – as remarked on by Herodotus – flashed into her head, and she marvelled at the power of the human brain to be so utterly incongruous. But then she herself was so absurdly, so tragically out of place. Nothing surprised her anymore.

How could a girl like her have come to this? Her eldest brother, now a lord, thriving in the family seat. Her middle sibling, a friar in the Franciscan order. A marriage into which she had no choice and which brought only cruelty. Her escape followed by poverty followed by prostitution, each step as inevitable as footfalls in the snow. She had visited her middle brother, Luc the friar, a few times, but never let him know who she really was, for fear that he too would reject her. That, and the desire to protect them both from knowledge of what she had become. She'd visited him on some pretext or another just to hear his voice – to remember what safety felt like.

Her belly relieved, she groped her way back to the thoroughfare, and once more the faces of the crowd came at her, veering into her vision like gargoyles on the cathedral wall. Some leered, some grimaced, most look frightened, all disgusted. They were a maelstrom, a storm. What had started as certain, individuated features became more and more indistinct, blurring into a whole. Before her eyes humanity was distilled into one identical expression; a tale of simple and profound distaste.

Her hand crept up to the side of her face, hesitated without touching, and fell back down to her side. She was afraid to feel, knowing that her fingers would only confirm what she already knew to be true. As if the crowd was not confirmation enough. Her tunic was wet; wet around the shoulders, down the front, wet over the patch that fell over her breasts. It hung heavily around her feet and she told herself that was the urine. But urine didn't drip and cause the thing to drag in the ground. She had lifted it high to avoid that.

Despite everything, she knew what it was she must do. She had to focus. She had to find the friar. That was all that mattered. That single line of thought contained within itself the only possibility left open, and in all that it rejected, it was liberating. Let the blood drip behind her, let the householders shut their doors and the people look away; she herself was all right – would be all right – if only her legs would last as long as she needed them, and her head keep good sense to guide them.

She could no longer stay upright, so she could no longer make her way unsupported down the street. The walls of the buildings held her up and she could see her progress at intervals, as if looking down on the scene. She saw it all; her dirty fingers, the nails encased with blood, clawing and clutching at the stone; clumps of hair torn out and the rest dangling disgracefully around her neck. She knew herself to be a pitiful sight but one that drew no pity – for no one cared. Her brain was losing focus. The friar! She must find the friar. Down the street. Did she make the turn by the wool mart or should she continue? Was that alley to the left a cut to the Priory? Was that cart going near him? Would it carry her? She looked for places she knew, and by great good fortune found them, as if her life had been a map with only this moment in mind. The forty foot house on her right, she remembered that all right! The merchant housed within, his braies around his ankles. Then, on towards the stocks and the tavern with rushes on the floor, lights and laughter within. On again, past the alms house, vision blurring now, the street rushing up to meet her as if a bed of hay. It felt so soft. The dirt and the stone, so soft. How could they feel like this, like the down feathers of her childhood bed? A light searing into her face. Her body rising and falling. At last, a face bending into hers. The sound of gates drawing back.

Somehow the girl had made it and her journey was at an end. She closed her eyes and a single tear made a sneaking progress into the wound that was once her hairline. It was instantly engulfed by blood.

The gatehouse porter was more shocked than he let on. 'Found her in the filth,' the carter said, as he escorted him to the back of the dung cart, from which the girl's arm trailed on the road. 'Looks like she's been damaged, and badly so. She breathed the name of Friar Luc but that was all she had.'

The porter nodded grimly, 'Ay, Friar Luc's here, though there'll be nought he can do with this.' The gorge rose within him and he didn't have the power to quell it. 'It was good of you to bring her,' he muttered, pressing a coin into the shit smeared fist. 'Another would have left her there.' The man touched his bare head and together they lifted the girl and carried her into the gatehouse, placing her on the stone ledge covered with straw that served as his permanent bed.

'She'll rest here while I fetch the friar. There's no strength in her for more.'

Having eased off his sandals and starting an inspection of his well-travelled feet, Luc had been irritated when Aurensis reappeared. 'What do you mean the porter needs me? Haven't I just come in and not eaten or washed since morning?' he grumbled. 'Who would be brave enough to need me in such a state?' But there was something in Aurensis' look that told him that jesting was not in order, and he'd followed him quickly enough. 'A badly wounded girl you say? Well I've seen enough of those in my time, and the wounds are always made by their men.' Luc had been a healer ever since he had been a friar, and he was well loved by the people of the town who brought their children and sometimes their beasts to the man whose robust frame hid a gentle heart. He couldn't always cure them but he nearly always made them feel better, whatever the result.

So, he was less shocked than the others when he stood before the girl and saw the extent of her injuries, which were horrific enough it was true. He ushered both Aurensis and the porter, gaping and inquisitive, out of the door and turned to examine her, wiping his hands on his tunic before he did so.

'What devil has been at work here?' he muttered, as with a downwards movement he tore the tunic at the neck. Her left breast had been completely severed so that it dangled under her arm, held on by just a slither of skin. The mutilation was as heavy and barbaric as that done to any beast, yet this girl was but in her twenties. Luc felt the anger start to rise as he examined her wounds.

The girl's head and face were partly covered by the yellow hood of the prostitute, and it was only when he drew it away that Luc stepped back in horror. The entire left side of her face had been cut away in a diagonal slice that exited at the point of her chin. The wound spurted with blood and the girl's tongue prodded repeatedly in the hole that was once her mouth, feeling the teeth in a steady compulsive movement. For the merest second Luc had the sense that he recognised her, but then he saw so many people. Though not like this; these wounds were those of a monster.

'This is the Devil's own work!' he said out loud. 'Satan himself!' He looked around helplessly. What use were his potions or balms in the face of such distress? He had not the skill to operate, and even if he had, what could he do? In all his years, Luc had never seen such a gross violation to a woman. These were the kinds of wounds normally delivered by war.

The girl was drifting in and out of consciousness and, at the same time, trying to talk. He knelt down beside her and took the tiny wrist in his hand.

'You're safe now, my child,' he muttered, not daring to stroke her hair lest the movement cause her agony. 'Say your confession and all will be well. I will not ask who did this.'

'My lord,' she replied faintly.

'Your confession,' he repeated more urgently, and then hated himself for asking it. She was barely conscious, how could she rehearse her life's mistakes? 'Then I will do it for you. We will do it together,' said the friar, clasping both her hands firmly in his.

'Our Father,' he started, then hesitated. What should he say? This girl was a harlot, a whore, she was probably a thief, might even be a murderess, for something had incited this violence. She was a true daughter of Eve; temptress, seducer, Jezebel. That was what his learning told him, but Luc had no time for his learning. For more than anything, the girl stilled in agony before him was a human being; a child of Heaven, however fallen. What should he say? What words would suffice to shield her, to allow her to slip unnoticed into her Father's house?

'Jacques.'

'What!' He had not been called by his birth name since he took holy orders twenty years ago.

'Jacques. *C'est moi…* Tantou.' Luc scanned the face again, unable to comprehend what she was saying. Tantou was his baby sister, a child he had last seen in the apple orchard of his father's manor, waving him on his journey. She had been four. What had this creature, this dismembered harlot, to do with a waving child?

'*C'est moi…*' she whispered again, her eyes trying to open.

'Tantou?' If Luc's world had been intact, it came crashing down in that instant. He had missed his family so much in the early years that he had invented a parallel world where they existed, much as they always had, shielded from the misfortunes of life. He had heard that first his father and then his mother had died, that his baby sister was married and his brother come into his inheritance, but all this had happened serenely and in the proper course of things. For him they were eternally bathed in the glow of his own safe childhood. This could not be Tantou, here in the filth; a whore, with one side of her face sliced away.

He released her hands abruptly and stepped back, seeing again the child with an apple the size of her fist, waving in the exaggerated fashion of the very young.

'You lie!' he hissed, for some things are sacred even for a friar. 'You speak untruth. Damn you!'

But the girl was becoming more agitated, her hands moving over her robe attempting to find his. She moved her head and moaned.

'All right! Then name my brother.' She was in no state to be questioned, but Luc found his pity had retreated.

She didn't answer and Luc turned away. Damn the whore. He would mutter a confession and leave her to the ministrations of her master. He prepared a poultice of arnica and rue.

'Guillaume!' Had she said that, or was it just the breeze creeping through the window?

'Again?' he said roughly, bending his ear low. 'Was it you that spoke or the Devil, your superior?'

The girl forced herself to open her eyes and locked his with her own. 'Guillaume,' she said again, with the most extraordinary effort. 'My brother…brother…is… Guillaume!'

Luc found that the earth he walked on had suddenly given way. 'And our mother?' He wasn't sure what prompted him.

The girl closed her eyes again. 'Melise,' she breathed, and Luc had to tear himself away and leave her for a moment. He stumbled out of the gatehouse and leant against the wall, the world spinning and his gut announcing that it was fit to spill. He looked around, hoping for something familiar, some order and certainty. But for once there was nothing to be seen. The soft summer day had gone black and bad. The sky was empty. There was no presence or goodness in the vastness, no gift in the small white clouds. God had left his Heaven and was somewhere very far away. Too far for Luc to see clearly, too far to be seen at all.

* * *

In a flash the only thing that mattered was to get back to her. He came to, finding himself slumped on the ground in a low squat with his back against the wall. What was he doing? Why was he sitting here when he should be with his sister?

She had shifted her position slightly. Turned her head, so all he saw was the wound when he wanted to see the person.

'Tantou? Can you hear me? I'm here. Forgive me. I see you. I'm here *ma petite*. Tantou!' She made a small movement though he was not sure she was conscious, so he tried again.

'Jacques; your brother.' He knew full well that he was not supposed to speak like that. Who was his mother or his brothers when he had shunned the world? But when it came to it, the instruction meant nothing compared to his own flesh and blood lying here, on the straw. Blood, and too much of it, all around.

She moaned again and looked at him, seeing him clearly for the first time. In a hurried, grasping gesture, he searched for her hand and held it.

'I'm here. Tell me if you can, tell me what is this, the hood and the blood? Who has done this to you?'

She really couldn't speak; it was all she could do to breathe. The pain was such that it was almost an incidental, so engrossing that she almost had a choice whether to sink in to it or not. With an act of uncommon will, she rose above it, to whisper in short, staccato sentences the highlights, if such they were.

'Goddard.' Luc nodded. He remembered the coarse kinsman who had visited from time to time. Surely his sister had not been married to a man four times her age?

'Your husband?'

'From the start… beatings. Worse.' She closed her eyes, seeing him again bearing down on her, pinning her by the hair as he manoeuvred her to begin another long assault. 'I could not refuse. When I tried…' Luc nodded again, hating the law that made a woman the property of her husband, to be used – and hurt – as he alone saw fit.

'So…?' he probed gently, seeing it all as if she were a player on the stage. 'You suffered it for years, until it was no longer an option. And then you left?'

The girl opened her eyes sharply, seeming to shut him down. '*Non*… child.'

'You had a child?'

She nodded, tears once more sliding unbidden down the wound that was once a face. She could not speak, so Luc could only imagine what the man had done to the child.

'And then you left?' She didn't answer so Luc filled in the gaps. The abuse; the death perhaps of the child. Her escape from a life of terror, exchanging it for one of shame. Who knew how long she had wandered? And then this. He forced himself to look again at the wounds. Were these done by a drunken client, a man she'd infected or spurned? Somehow he doubted it. These were not the wounds of casual wrong; this horror was meant and determined. And then he knew. This was the final beating, the mark of the husband wronged. This was done by his kinsman!

'Goddard did… this?'

But there was no response.

From nowhere she screamed; a terrifying, pain-wracked scream that split the air of the little room, fracturing it. She screamed again, the pain gashing into her consciousness like one on a rack or stake. It was unbearable.

Luc looked around. There was nothing here other than the cloth of paste he carried from his girdle. That was for cuts and scrapes, not for the likes of this. In a sudden action he got up and tore himself away, hoping she would not notice his absence. His mind was whirling but he had to find some way to ease her suffering, and that needed herbs; his own chests where the potent ones were stored. He knew it would ease the pain, the herbs he crushed quickly and methodically – monkshood, henbane, gentian and belladonna – in such a cocktail as to put her to sleep in an hour, and kill her in a day. She was asleep when he returned, with the grey paste diluted in water which he put on the shelf beside her, its deadliness as much a horror as a salve. He would not wake her. Maybe God would work a miracle.

For the rest of the evening she slept. And she continued to sleep, restless and fitfully, but nevertheless out of pain, throughout the night. Luc didn't. He sat beside her, studying her, till he knew from memory the exact way her eyebrow curved, the number of tiny lines in the otherwise perfect skin and the childish tilt of her nose. All this on the good side, of course. Not the wounded one. Not the one where the blood continued to flow, sluggishly now, in a slow black stream.

She woke, finally, in the morning, as the sun was making its graceful assent and mirroring itself in her eyes. Before the pain could hit her, he poured the dilution into her mouth, her tongue seeming to take it with gratitude, though its taste must have been bitter.

'This will take the pain,' he murmured, and then as an afterthought, 'and it will carry you home.'

For the rest of the morning he knelt there, holding her hands as the warmth gradually left them, and pouring little drops of fluid into her mouth each time her eyes told him of pain. It was a long vigil. She could talk very little, so Luc did the talking for her, recalling her childhood and their parents in the dappled orchard of his memory. He filled it with beauty, being careful not to mention Goddard.

He kept his tone light though his throat was closed. He spoke of Gentil, the old carthorse, on whose back he had held her before she could even walk. 'So, you could ride before you could crawl,' he said, trying to be merry and resting his head by her side. She seemed to understand, seemed to like this realm of make-believe that would have been so true had the future not cancelled it out.

Then, at around midday, just as he was describing the great hall where they slept with the dogs and servants, she made an effort to speak.

'Track… up track.'

'The track leading to the hundred hectares?'

'Steep!' She winced, as if her face reflected the effort of climbing the track as she must have done so often when a child. Then, suddenly, the same face relaxed as if the effort was finished and won.

'Aagh!'

'What can you see?' he whispered, pouring the last drop of anaesthetic into the sloping side of her mouth. But she didn't answer; caught up, as she was, in whatever vision of loveliness laid spread out beneath her. She breathed one last time, struggled momentarily and then her body went limp. Death had claimed her and her anguish could not now reappear.

He stood up, shakily, unsure as to whether he had committed a sin. But in his heart he knew that even if he had, it were a sin he would have had to embrace, whatever the Church Fathers taught.

**

University of Paris: Six weeks later

The novice who'd brought him to a great wooden door, fretted with heavy ironwork, bowed and drifted away. Luc was left standing, his arm raised to knock. He found himself hesitating for just a fraction longer than he might. It was many years since he had seen the great scholar, and Thomas Aquinas was not known as a sociable man. No doubt he would resent the intrusion. Still, when last they had met he had been tolerant enough of his company. And the hour was early.

He knocked. Almost immediately, he heard the scraping of a chair and the turning of the key in the lock. The door opened to reveal a brightly lit room almost entirely blocked by the enormous figure that now stood in front of him, peering short-sightedly into the gloom.

'Your eminence. If I disturb you please tell me, but I heard you were returned to Paris and wished to pay my respects.' Luc bowed low and Aquinas shook his head.

'No, no, not at all. My work is no great matter. Please do come in.' The refined accent of a well-bred nobleman couldn't really hide itself, despite the friar's cloth, as the large but graceful man made a motion for Luc to enter. The room was bright because it was lit by a dozen tallow candles perched on every available surface. The master's window was ajar, and every so often a breeze ruffled the stillness, disturbing piles of parchment. Luc's mouth fell open in wonder. Was all the learning in the world contained in this little room? Everywhere around were scrolls and folios. On the floor, on shelves, in the open trunk; the entire space overflowing with books and manuscripts, the likes of which he had never seen.

Thomas walked quickly over to his writing desk and secured a sheaf of thin parchment which threatened to blow all over the floor. 'The Manuscript of Christomisys,' he said, running his hand lovingly over the vellum. 'For many years I have yearned for this, and just today I have acquired it. The treasures contained within are still a mystery.'

Luc nodded. He felt out of place among the erudition but the great man had such an air of scholarly distractedness that he assumed his own rustiness would go unnoticed. He still wasn't sure why he'd come, but he trusted that his inner voice would be proved right – eventually – by whatever came to pass.

'We have met before, some years ago. I accompanied you and Friar Bonaventura when we travelled to Rome. It is a long time now and you may not recall…'

'Ah, but I do.' Aquinas relaxed, now that he could place his visitor. 'Indeed I do! We went to plead that our order of travelling friars should not be banned and we won, though the best arguments were made by our friend. I myself spoke but little, though my size perhaps added some weight!' He laughed, with the self-conscious air of one unused to being a wit, and Luc guffawed in appreciation. He often found that his own ready laugh eased a shy man miraculously.

'Not at all, not at all. But tell me, Master, do I really not disturb you?'

Thomas opened his hands as if to say, 'You are disturbing me but I've resigned myself to that,' though actually he said nothing at all other than, 'Call me your brother, for that I am. Come, shall we walk?'

The students, who lived in rooms and lodgings as close to the lectures as possible, thronged the narrow streets beyond Aquinas' window. Housed within the university precincts, the great scholar was relatively shut off from the noise and clamour of the town, but he bore it bravely as they stepped on to the swarming street. This area was almost unknown to Luc and he was immediately aware of the vigour and purpose in the faces, so unlike the poor among whom he passed his time. They were an unruly lot; jostling and pushing, shouting over each other, spilling out of the taverns. Almost immediately, the middle-aged friars ran into a mock fight between two combatants armed with wooden daggers. The general hullabaloo was heightened by troubadours and street performers with viols, rebecs and drums. It felt a festival, though it was just the every day.

'What it is to be young,' Luc shouted above the clamour.

'Indeed. I have often thought that the most hopeful people in the world are the young and the drunk. The first because they have little experience of failure, and the second because they have succeeded in drowning theirs!' replied Aquinas.

Luc laughed, genuinely this time. 'But you have little experience of failure, good brother. I have heard that you have twice been professor, and might be again?'

'And what a fate that would be! But, for the meantime, I am more than content, immersed in my books and my philosophy.'

'Then we are both blessed,' said Luc. 'For while you study the salvation of our souls, I minister to the diseased bodies that house them.'

The great man smiled but said nothing, as if he hadn't quite heard.

'And the more I see,' Luc continued, 'the more I am convinced that our petty frames are so insignificant – mere charnel houses. So often I see the soul blaze forth when the body is at its most decrepit. I don't know about you but I've often seen life in death as well as death in life, and it never ceases to astound me.'

'That is because you are a mystic,' said the great man, crossing the street to avoid a fire-eating fakir who was pulling in a crowd. 'At heart all you want is to dissolve yourself in the infinite, whereas I see God as essentially Other.'

Luc nodded. Aquinas' work was something of a talking point, verging as it did on heresy. 'You are reading the Ancients?'

'Aristotle? Yes! One of the few good things to have come out of the recent crusade. And I find that great pagan mind of his can still speak to us even today, telling us that we all have a final cause. A purpose, if you like; more unique and compelling than any other of God's creations.'

'And that purpose is...? To fulfil what He intends us to be?'

It was Aquinas' turn to nod in assent. 'To seek good and avoid evil, in accordance with our heavenly nature, so that we may at last see Him – the one who constructed us all.'

Luc was eyeing a courtier dressed as a popinjay and strutting his padded hose. He hesitated before he spoke again, for he was as sure as he could be that what he was about to say really was heresy, and this was something important to him.

'My brothers tell me that you deny evil?'

Aquinas stopped in his tracks and faced him.

'That's a very superficial assessment. A charge so paupered it turns dangerous.'

30

'You don't deny evil?'

'I deny it, perhaps, as you understand it. Let me explain. If God is wholly simple then there is just no place for evil. He cannot have created evil, and He cannot allow it to exist alongside His nature, which is one of simple, unified goodness. But evil exists, most certainly it does. All I am saying is that evil is what happens when a man turns away from God. He can no longer discern the path. Of course I don't deny evil, just perhaps the way it is commonly understood. To my mind, evil is what happens when a man mistakenly pursues his own end and cannot see God's.'

Luc breathed a little in relief. He could understand that.

'You must never do a wrong action, even for a good consequence,' the great man was continuing. 'Sometimes evil dresses itself up as a consequence saying, "If I do such and such – a bad thing – for such and such else – a good thing – then it matters little", but that is wrong. Quite wrong!' Aquinas slapped his hand across his chest in a curiously Roman manner. 'That would be evil; for intention matters and conscience matters. And an act matters more than its consequences.'

Luc was thinking of his sister. 'But sometimes I give a drug that will take away the pain or relieve the symptoms. But it's strong. The pain may be quelled but the heart will weaken and so, in effect, I shorten life. Is that a good act or a bad one?'

Aquinas looked at him. 'Your intention when you give the medicine is to relieve the pain?'

'Most sure.'

'Then it is a good act, and the fact that life is shortened merely an unwelcome effect.'

Luc was not quite sure. He wanted to be certain that he

fully understood. 'Even if I know the consequence when I foresee the result? How can I not intend something to happen when I know by my actions it will? Surely knowing something, means that I intend it in some way?'

Aquinas squared up to him and placed his hand on Luc's shoulder.

'You are a good man. Listen to your conscience and follow it. As long as what you intend is a good act then no harm can come by it, and you are not in sin. Only when you *intend* an evil is that sin, and then it is venal and vile. It is not your fault that a single action can have many effects.'

Luc relaxed, this was what he had hoped he would hear.

'Then, can I ask you one other thing?' he said, quietly prepared to ask with or without permission. 'On what are our laws based?' He was thinking again of his sister and the law that, somehow, had failed her.

Aquinas glanced at him sharply, as if Luc had impressed him.

'A natural law' he said, 'Written into the human heart, even when our customs obscure it. That is what you have sensed.' He smiled shyly from his great height.

A street seller lunged up, his tray of sweetmeats filling the air with the pungent smell of roast flesh. Aquinas stepped aside and Luc felt like kicking the fellow into the gutter, even though his nostrils twitched and flared. They had been on the brink of something important – he could have touched it. Could have understood. And now the moment had been broken by the smell of roast pork and barley.

'A natural law?' he said at last, tentatively.

Aquinas nodded. 'Written into your heart.'

'Shared by everyone? Common to all?'

'Yes!'

They stopped and looked at each other as the throng of humanity surged past; the faces vacant or intent. Each one about its business, hardly noticing the two men of God. And unaware of what had been said. Or how important it might be.

* * *

The call to prayer came while it was still dark, before the birds knew it was time to greet the day. The slow, rhythmic sound of the bell rolled its way around the building, entering the cells of the friars and calling them together in worship. Some were already awake, kneeling on the floor, locked in conversation with the Friend to whom they had long since given their life. Others roused themselves unhurriedly, pulling the brown surplice over the white undergarment, sluicing faces and heads in pitchers of water placed in the corner of their rooms. Though it was dark outside, the faintest hint of the sun could be detected as Luc opened his shutters and drank in a draught of night air. It was not light, but the hint of light; the night giving way to the day.

As he left his cell, Luc kept his mind focused on the still point that he had attained the night before. Although the anger was still there, bitter and insistent, he buried it as best he might. It remained the only thing he could do.

One by one, the friars assembled in the church. Even though his eyes never left the floor, Luc was aware of the presence of each as they entered. The church was a nest. Every one of the men assembled there came with a gift, was himself a gift, though to the eye of the world, the friars looked as identical as a clutch of eggs laid by a nesting hen. Luc could sense his brothers without seeing them. He could sense, too, when there was no one else to come. A sufficiency, a quota, an authenticity that made them complete. Only when the last man was there – old Aurensis with his peculiar shuffling step – did Prior Christophe stand and face the altar as a cue for the service to begin. Together, the Friars of the University of Paris turned towards the cross and began the liturgy. The familiar words, the chant and responses, as alive and personal as the Christ child itself.

PATER noster, qui es in caelis, sanctificetur nomen tuum. Adveniat regnum tuum. Fiat voluntas tua, sicut in caelo et in terra.

Though he had said this as many times as he had tasted bread, the words never failed to explode in Luc. Just occasionally they let him down and spoke only of the improbability of faith. On those days they were bitter as gall.

It was only after the last 'Amen', when the friars returned to their cells, that Luc allowed the world to come flooding in. He pushed back the shutters, hearing them creak as he fastened the iron clasp and saw the great city spread beneath him. From a peg on the wall he took down a wicker basket and examined the contents. A jar of aloe, an ointment made from balsam, arnica for bruises, and a bottle of vinegar in a beaker of fired clay. He took some dried roots and burr seeds and placed those in the basket along with a pestle and mortar. Lastly, he plucked the rosary from his bed where it had lain throughout the night, and hung it from the rope round his waist.

Why was the porter looking at him peculiarly? Had he forgotten something?

'Prior wants to see you!' the man muttered as he passed.

'He said nothing at the service.'

'He's saying it now!'

Leaving his things in the gatehouse, which he hadn't

entered since the death of Tantou, Luc made his way to the prior's lodging. He had no fear of Father Christophe and reflected that he'd most probably be asked to undertake another tedious journey.

Father Christophe was standing by the window. He didn't, at first, turn round.

'You've a visitor.'

'Father?'

The Prior didn't move. He was staring, intently, outdoors.

'A guest has come – for you!' Luc looked down. It was unheard of, to be summoned like this.

'You may see him in my Lodging.' There was no malice in the Prior's voice but it was laced with something that Luc could not quite place. Something foreign to the man that bordered on mistrust.

'I will be about the Abbey,' he said and Luc was suddenly alone. A heavy curtain separated this room from the Prior's inner parlour – a place reserved for the most important guests. And Luc sensed whom he would find.

Aquinas was seated at a bench by the window. He stared at his feet, in the manner of one equally surprised to find himself in this situation, and rose as Luc entered.

'I came,' he said, 'because you sought me when groping for a very small truth. But a truth despite that. And it matters that you find it.'

The room was dark and badly lit and, from nowhere, Luc felt tears spring abruptly behind his eyes. He frowned, his forehead creasing as he fought to hold them back. The sudden warmth, the unexpected connection, hit him sharply and made him less than manly. He had not expected this; the great man coming to find him. Aquinas lowered his gaze and pretended not to have seen.

'What is it that fulfils you?' he asked, sitting down again with a degree of heaviness and gesturing for Luc to do likewise. 'If it's not too direct a question? What prompts and motivates you?' Luc studied the calluses of his fingers; aware that this kind of intimacy was against the other man's nature. And more grateful than he knew how to show.

'To serve,' he said simply, trying to be honest. 'As our Lord did. To reach out and find Him in the poor.'

'And do you?' Aquinas' voice was too light and insubstantial to be housed in such a frame. The damasks on the walls absorbed all the air, so there was a closeness in the room that charged their speech. 'Find Him?' Luc had a sudden impulse to run.

'Not often,' he replied after a second or too. He was aware that it was impious. Rude, as well, to be answering so obliquely. 'I used to…..' his voice trailed off and the stabbing behind the eyes reasserted itself so hard that he blinked and frowned again. 'I had a sister,' he continued. 'She's dead now.' He was all too conscious that this was nothing – death was everywhere, and what was a sister to him?

Aquinas waited, absorbed in some far-away thought.

'And the point is… That she was imperfect. She was sullied and lost. She was far from perfection. And I couldn't see God the more I looked – all I could see was a girl!' He glanced in the direction of the black robe. 'If God is at our centre, where is He when we go wrong?'

He had the sense that Aquinas waited, not because he was thinking of an answer. Not because he was constructing it. He was simply waiting. It seemed an age before he spoke, and when he did, it was with a hesitancy that had nothing to do with doubt. But it had allowed space for Luc's own to grow.

'God is Other,' Aquinas said, picking his words with care.

'He allows us our freedom. Of that I am sure. Without freedom man is reduced. Without freedom man cannot.....' his voice trailed off and Luc needed, once more, to wait.

'Cannot?' he prompted, indelicately.

The black robe glanced over with a quick, well-hidden impatience.

'Cannot be itself,' he answered.

Luc nodded – he was used to this Platonic ideal. That man must search for perfection – a Reality that evaded them all.

'Our perfect self,' he said without enthusiasm – a vision of Tantou appearing without warning.

Aquinas shifted himself and turned to the Franciscan.

'No,' he said. 'I meant the opposite. We are different – all of us. And we are free. But we share a common nature and we share a common goal. You desire to seek God, and in that you are not far from me. Your search will make you content.'

Luc harrumphed, wondering how true that actually was and whether he would not be more content to be out with Sabine on the hillside. But he let it pass.

'I would like to know that I've done my best,' he said unaffectedly. 'I would like Him to know that.'

'It's a progression,' continued Aquinas, opening his arms in an awkward arc. 'Not downwards from some Perfect Form. That's what the Staggirite tells me.'

'Aristotle?'

'The same. There are some conditions – some states of being – that allow us to fulfil that impulse and best allow us to grow. Like a plant that thrives in good soil.'

Luc was silent, watching a spider spin its silver in the deepest corner of the room.

'It is those conditions that make up the natural law; the

elements in which a man can thrive. It is this that underpins us. That everyone needs. What does the common man want?'

Luc felt like saying that most men wanted just one thing – and it was something the Church disapproved of, but Aquinas beat him to it.

'I know,' he said with that same confident diffidence that sat so awkwardly together. 'He wants his life and his women – or more importantly, to pass on his seed. He wants his offspring to flourish and to do that he needs to have order. And he wants to worship his God. That is the general condition – and it follows that that is the natural law.'

'So…. the law comes from our natures?' Luc was hesitant.

'It does. Put there – instilled – from the first. Why else could Augustine say "Lex iniusta non est lex"?'

'An unjust law is no law at all,' translated Luc. 'There must be a natural Law for an unjust law to jar.'

'Indeed,' said the older man, locking him for the first time in an unabashed gaze. 'Above any human law, whether unjust or right. Now shall we go and find your sister?'

Luc was about to say, "I have no sister and I've no idea what you mean," when he thought better of it and put down his guard. The man had come to find him – the greatest scholar of the age. If God had allowed him to read his heart – and for the life of him Luc couldn't think how else the other could know – there was suddenly nothing to hide. He led him out into the garden and through the herbs which the brothers were tending, down to the mossy graves of the laymen, set in the meadow apart from the Church where all the good monks were interred.

'This is her,' he said, gesturing at the turf still standing proud with her body. 'Where she lies. She was a whore.'

38

He let the words out with a rush of breath, hating the sound they made, that travestied her but that were also true.

'She repented?' Luc listened for the note of revulsion in the scholar's question, but found none. At least none that satisfied him. He grunted ambiguously. To bury her unconfessed in consecrated ground was against the law of the Church and every known convention. But she hadn't repented as such.

He nodded obliquely and Aquinas studied his feet. There was a simple wooden cross at the head of her grave, uninscribed. Luc had fettled it himself and placed it in a private ceremony, alone and under the sky.

'There are some things,' continued Aquinas in that same level tone with just the hint of something querulous lying not far behind, 'That should be done, even when they sit badly with the age in which they happen. Antigone knew it. You do too, I suspect.'

Luc levelled him with his eyes and didn't flinch. He cocked his head back suddenly, as if he'd been jerked by something, but his eyes didn't leave those of his eminent guest. A hundred years could have fallen and he still would have held his gaze as Aquinas spoke.

'And the rules that we think are rules, have no weight if they go against the core of our being. The core that makes us ourselves.'

'Different people, different cores,' shrugged the man in the brown cowl of the Franciscans, whose face and body were as hardened as an acorn that has lain too long in the sun. Who didn't care for the answer.

'Different people, *same* core,' said his Dominican companion with a soft smile. 'Same core. That is the truth you were after. That's the one you must know.'

They had been travelling for days; a small procession making their way through the rutted lanes and uneven tracks of the kingdom's southern states. Some years had passed and Luc was once more in the presence of Aquinas, older now and travelling to attend the Council at Lyons with little more than the sun in the sky and an unreliable chart to steer them.

They were a strange little band; Aquinas sat, almost entirely silent, astride a stout grey donkey that had been specially loaned to carry his weight. Luc and Sabine, also older, were accompanied by the boy Uthier who had, of late, shown interest in joining 'God's Beggars', as the Friars were known. This was his first trip away from home and every new village was a wonder. He had grown much in the preceding years and his natural timidity given way to an open, sensitive face, perpetually tanned and perpetually awake; for youth lives much in the moment.

'How is he?' muttered Luc, addressing the boy who towered above him, leading Sabine with the use of neither switch nor violence.

'Much the same.'

They exchanged glances. It was a very different scholar who they were escorting to represent his mother Church.

'Does he speak?'

Uthier shook his head. 'Not since this morning and that was not clearly at all.'

They both looked round at the big man, who followed some distance behind, swaying slightly on his mount, with a fixed and empty expression.

'Do you think he suffers, Brother?' asked Uthier, as if he'd pondered the question for a long time.

'If that's suffering then I'll have some!' replied the older man good naturedly, grunting slightly as his knees felt the journey.

'But he is so very changed. Almost a different being.'

'Ay,' said Luc, stopping to admire a bough of cherry blossom and at the same time ease his sandals. 'What beauty is all around!'

'You shield him brother,' said Uthier, 'You have done all the journey. Tell me, I beg, what this is all about. Let me in on his secret!'

'I would,' replied Luc, replacing the offending footwear 'Were it not that it's his and therefore not mine to tell!'

'Dare I ask him?'

'I don't know – do you? Is it for one to pry into the secret heart of another, when that heart wishes to remain closed? If Brother Aquinas wishes to speak, he will do so in his own good time. If he does not, you will have to bear it and stifle that snuffling nose!' Luc laughed contentedly, remembering what it felt like to be young.

'I daresay he will,' he added, relenting slightly. 'When he returns from his wanderings. For now, he has much to see.'

Uthier was content with that; knowing, as he did, that the Brother spoke of the internal wanderings of the scholar's mind and not some place on the distant horizon. It was only much later, when they had pitched camp, erected a shelter beneath a pine tree and lit an adequate fire that Uthier returned to the subject again.

'Are you well, good Brother?'

Aquinas looked startled, as if he were waking from a very deep dream. He smiled, benignly but said nothing.

Uthier tried again. 'Is there anything we can do for you? Letters to write maybe, or notes for the next work you expect to undertake?'

Aquinas shook his head and fixed the teenager with a look of the utmost intensity.

'I will not write again.'

Luc, stirring the ashes round the fire, looked away as if he were unwilling to witness the scene.

Uthier said nothing but similarly picked up a stick so as to have some little task to do. He felt he was on the precipice of another man's soul, and rather wished he had not pushed to get there.

'I will not write again. For all I have written seems as utter straw compared to what I have seen.'

'The Doctor was praying,' explained Luc gruffly, irritated with the youth who had forced the private matter. 'He was shown a vision.'

'Which I can never begin to explain,' Aquinas added, quite soberly and not like one in the grip of hysteria. 'But it revealed to me the extent of the Glory of God and all my writings, all my thought, are as nothing compared to what was revealed. So now I am silenced. Content only to watch and wait, knowing the Mystery – or its taste, at the least.'

That night the great scholar sickened, thoroughly and without warning. They had not the time to reach the South of France so, between them, Luc and Uthier managed to strap him to the donkey and bring him to the House of Fossanova nestling, as it was, in the green fields. It was there that the great scholar passed away, simply and without fuss, wrapped in the glory of the Absolute that only his eyes and his great faith saw. It was Luc who heard his confession and he emerged with tears streaming down his face and shaking his head in disbelief.

'What is it Brother? What ails you?' Uthier had run up, concerned.

'On the contrary. Nothing ails me' he paused to admire a rose tree and was silent a while before adding, 'He said his confession like a child. This man who has written a thousand works, a mind steeped in learning, the father of the morrow's Church, prayed, at the end, with no more art than an infant.'

Uthier looked astonished, and perhaps a little disappointed. 'Is that not truly strange,' he began, 'The greatest man of our generation, with no words at all at the last?'

But Luc was shaking his head. 'Not strange at all,' he muttered, smiling in unhasty joy. 'Not strange at all. In fact – just what I would expect. Just what it's all about.' And with that he got up, whistled to Sabine who was grazing, and turned to walk away, to spend half an hour in the fields, quietly and on his own.

* * * * * * * *

Chesterton let out his breath in a long sigh. 'Marvellous,' he said. 'Quite marvellous. That's why Catholicism is so healthy. It gives man a sense of purpose – he is clamouring to see his God.' He smiled in the genuine warmheartedness of his faith, which embraced story and wisdom in one overarching truth. The book, lying open beside him, appeared to bask in his praise.

'Nothing but sickness!' spat Nietzsche, who had been engrossed in the scene despite his better judgement. 'A woman typical of her sex! Weak and undernourished. Afraid to embrace what she is! And the hypocrisy of the brother who'll bend the rules when they fail to serve his purpose. It's always that way with Religious. They are all hypocrites in the end.'

Chesterton opened his mouth to protest but Nietzsche was not yet finished. He flung one leg over the log on which he was sitting, with a quick and curious agility and bounced a little with frustration. The book closed suddenly shut.

'All this talk of fulfilment as if there's some kind of plan! A plan depends on a planner. But where will you find such a thing? The sky is empty of such. Instead you must study the people. The great men are different to the herds – I am different to you. There is no such thing as natural law for there is no nature we commonly share. All, as I said, is convention. The custom of time or place.'

'Lord! But you're blind. And if you're not blind you're stupid!' said Chesterton. 'The sane man knows that some things are a mystery. It's that knowledge that keeps him so sane.'

The two men sat and tried not to see each other, separated by different beliefs. Their very skins were a barrier. Whereas Chesterton was expansive and lively, his whole being given over to the sense of joy with which he embraced the world, Nietzsche sat shrivelled but alert.

'I like Luc and I like Aquinas,' the journalist continued. 'I intend to meet them both quite soon.' He took out a notebook and a gold leaf retractable pencil, and wrote the two names under the title "Theists – to Meet".

'You're just a God-botherer! There is no such thing as God! Why can't you see that – you have been up the mountain!' The German looked a little uncertain as he said it, for he realised that Chesterton *might* have seen God, but relaxed when he was not contradicted. 'And what's all this nonsense about chastity! Aquinas and Luc were both chaste – but how can that be healthy? Why take something so natural and turn it into a sin? There's no sin in using your body!'

It was the journalist's turn to look uneasy – for he happened to agree in part. He considered explaining chastity in terms of a vocation; that added rather than took something away, but doubted whether the German could hear it.

'And now, at last, it's my turn,' continued the German, spitting into his whiskers. 'Pass me the book! And we will see what we will see!'

Chesterton handed over the slim volume with some reluctance, as its tattered cover appeared to stiffen when placed in the hands of the German. Nietzsche handled it with none of the care it had come to know from the Englishman, and rifled through its pages impatiently.

'I will go with my last thoughts and roll out this chastity

business,' he mused. 'Let's see a man who knows about pleasure. Back to fifth century Greece and people who knew how to live. Are you coming with me, fat one? I made my studies in this.'

Chesterton shrugged, 'I suppose so. Show me what pleasure can do.'

'Very well then. Hold on to your seat. I'll show you a real sort of pleasure!' The wind grew more menacing as she flung the two figures forcefully back in time, murmuring quietly as she did so. The book clamped itself shut and fell between the two men, where it lodged itself tightly in Chesterton's shoe.

* * * * * * * *

ATHENS 290 BC

ARISTIPPUS OF CYRENE

Everyone said she was still beautiful. She was not too old to wear the lightest robe that hung gracefully over her body. Or sport the most beautiful sandals; her toenails lacquered and buffed to a shine. She kept her hair long, its dark stream held in place by a garland of flowers that her slave had prepared that morning, muttering, as he did every day, 'Beautiful mistress. Kali Dianthe.'

Outside, the city was engulfing. Noise and dust. People starting their journeys. The mules pulling carts piled high with fruit, as the sun rose on another hot day. Although she could not see it, she could hear the city stirring; the urchins shouting and darting, the women and the slaves. And the men, nursing thick heads from the previous night, grumbling and getting up.

She had seen it all, and she had left it all behind.

'What is it that everyone seeks? What is happiness? And who is happy?' The men she waited for in the garden claimed to know and she was here, once again, to listen. She loved these long discussions with these men of different persuasions – amidst the swollen fruit trees.

Dianthe kept her eyes fixed on a bee drinking deep from a flower and, for the first time in years, thought of her parents. They were peasants, whose perpetual scratching and scraping at the barren Attic soil had given them just enough strength to carry on scratching until, that is, the harvest had failed and they had given up – hung their hoes on the wall and sold their daughter into slavery, saying that it was either that or starvation. What had happiness meant to them? She recalled her mother offering weeds to the goddess when there was literally nothing else to give, laying them out so fearfully before slinking, shame faced, away. Happiness for her parents, Dianthe suspected, was only achieved at the *end* of a life, when the gods – whose chief amusement was the destruction of mortals – had somehow let them slip by.

A movement near the villa caused the woman to look up, and she rose as the men approached her. They were laughing and gesticulating as they made their way across the courtyard attended by several young slaves. Dianthe went to meet them.

Epicurus was, as usual, polite and completely at ease. He greeted her as he would a friend and gestured for her to be seated, wherever she chose among them.

'You knew a man who knew Plato!' he began, raising his right hand to indicate to the others to be quiet. New friends had joined them that day. 'We were talking of a certain Aristippus. A philosopher, or so he claimed. But he had been taught by the master. Or learned from him, at least.'

'I met Aristippus once,' she said resuming the previous day's talk. Yesterday's discussions had ended when his name had been mentioned. She had been thinking of him all night.

'Listen friends. Come join us and listen!' Epicurus waved at several late comers and while they made their way over, Dianthe let herself muse.

She'd been slave to a woman who ran a brothel.

She had been ten years old.

The man had stopped by the House of the Porne and stuck his head round the cheerful red door.

'Anyone here?'

Artemis had come from the room at the back. She was called Artemis after the goddess of hunting who is also the goddess of girls. This Artemis hunted girls.

'Ah, Aristippus,' she had said, kissing him on the cheeks in a light, familiar manner. 'A philosopher after my own heart. A true lover of sensation. What is it you desire? I have a new girl in, straight from the country, guaranteed clean and unbroken.'

'How young?' the man had sniffed the air, as if he could detect the rank scent of chastity.

'Young,' her mistress had replied. 'I guarantee it, she is intact.' The woman had been hetaera herself – an educated, cultured prostitute – but her status had fallen as age had increased, and she then ran a brothel instead. 'And several fresh-faced youths. Would a combination please you?'

Aristippus, the philosopher, had considered. He was a little jaded; his concubine Laius having exhausted him an hour ago. Still, why not?

'Bring them out, or better still have them bring me wine and I will make them dance a while.'

Artemis had bowed and clapped her hands. And that had been the signal. The young men had run past her, naked, except for garlands, each holding a pitcher of wine. Aristippus had allowed himself to be led to a couch. Dianthe remembered how he had eyed the dancers as one would consider a feast.

After a few minutes his appetite had wakened. 'The girl!' he had called. One of the youths came to get her. 'Dance!' he had whispered. So she had danced, clad only in a short cotton tunic and longing for her mother to appear at the door. But her mother never came and would never come. So she kept her eyes down and danced; bending low, lifting her arms, swooping and running before him. The young men clapped from the sidelines, beating her rhythm out quick.

With a click of his fingers, Aristippus had stopped her and motioned for her to approach. She'd done so, trembling, her heart doing somersaults and her face on fire.

'You!' he had called to one of the boys. 'Take her!' The boy had been startled and unsure.

'Sir?'

'It amuses me!' he had said and she remembered how seconds had passed before the sudden searing sensation as the slave boy entered her body.

Aristippus had watched, but not spoken.

'Do you feel pain?' the philosopher had asked.

She had nodded. 'Sir!' But it was his next words that had struck her and that she'd always remembered.

'I cannot experience your pain,' he'd said, 'Just as you cannot experience my pleasure. So your pain is nothing to me.'

She had nodded between sobs, biting on the hem of her garment which had been thrown up as she knelt.

'Enough! Let her go!' The slave had backed away and helped her to her feet, while blood trickled fast down her thigh.

'Do as you wish,' he had said. 'Go and sit in the sun and eat grapes, and I will pay your mistress. Go! I have never met you!'

'Sir?' she had said again.

'I have never met you,' the man had repeated, stroking

the other slave's head. 'I am not the same now as the man who entered the door. I will not be the same as the man who leaves by the door. The man who will be 'I' in five minutes, is not the 'I' of now! There is only the present, only this now. So *I* have not known *you*.' He had run his hand through the hair of the youth with a curiously tender motion.

'You – lad – are a philosopher,' he had said to the back of the head, as the youth bent down before him. 'For only a true philosopher knows that pleasure is the goal.' He had waved her away and allowed his head to fall back against the couch, engrossed in the waves of sensation.

Afterwards, he had tipped them an obol – she and the other lad seated on the step; two children let outdoors.

As he left, he'd called back over his shoulder, 'Happiness is yours if you claim it. But only through the senses. So gorge and whore and drink your way through life. There's nothing else!'

She had never forgotten those words. She still wondered if they could be right and it was that scene of long ago that had come back and coloured her night.

'And now we're all seated,' said Epicurus, his voice breaking her reverie. A slave boy approached and offered her wine which she noticed she sipped too quickly. But the urbane and cultured tone of her host continued without pause. She'd given nothing away.

'Plato would have said – as Aristippus, myself and even Zeno here might agree – that the goal of life is pleasure. "There is no need to ask why a man desires happiness." Those were the master's own words. But this was not enough for Plato; this brief and fleeting happiness. Human happiness is imperfect – always passing, and poor. Insufficient, this anxious mortal happiness. So, he invented a Form of Happiness; perpetually unattainable and perpetually true.'

Dianthe nodded. She had been attending these Epicurean meetings long enough to know something of this.

'In contrast, Aristippus held that pleasure was a thing of the senses,' she offered, rehearsing her memories of moments before. 'He had no time for virtue. His was an earthy bliss. There was no shame in the fleeting sensation. To quest for anything else somehow defeated the quest.'

One of the older men grunted. 'Bah – that's a poor, sorry thing'.

'For me there's nothing particularly wrong with it!' laughed Epicurus who habitually commanded attention, while Zeno the Stoic shuffled his feet. 'I've nothing against the flesh. But it's not enough for happiness! You were hetaera,' her host continued, turning back to Dianthe whose face was shaded from the sun. 'The most cultured of all courtesans. There are none of the sensual arts you don't know. Tell us – all of us assembled here. Does perpetual pleasure bring happiness?'

'It can't do,' replied Dianthe. 'For else, why am I here? Why do any of us aim for a higher life if pleasure is all we crave? I have slaves, wine and a fine house. Money, jewels and more. Yet I am restless – out there in the city. There's a surfeit, already, of jewels.'

Epicurus smiled. 'What we need to understand,' he said, as he once more took centre stage, 'is that happiness is not the same as peace of mind. Happiness is too closely aligned to pain; the pain of getting it wrong. I could teach in the Agora. And yet I spend my time here; with you in this garden. It brings me a gentle pleasure that allows me to be whole. It's no hardship not to have the richest food that will make me sick. It's no hardship not to visit a courtesan for the third or fourth time in a day! In everything, the state of satiation is not nice. Which is why I say, it is peace of mind that counts."

'How can we ever know that, when we're all heading straight towards our deaths?' asked an old man in the company. 'I am old now and it won't be long. And it frightens me, dying, I'll tell you straight and undermines all that I do.'

'Why does it frighten you, friend?' said Epicurus, as all eyes turned to the citizen.

'I'm frightened of the beyond. And if there is no beyond, then I'm frightened of not existing.'

'And therein lies your mistake,' said the philosopher, 'In assuming that the same consciousness that you now enjoy will be present at the time of your death. While you exist there is no death. When you no longer exist, then there is death. But there is no single second when you both exist and die. So, there is nothing to fear.'

The old man looked a little comforted.

Zeno could no longer be silent.

'Our friend is right in so much,' he bellowed, for his voice carried over them all. 'But he stops too soon. For where are the gods in this? Although he speaks of them sometimes, he allows them no power; they don't alter his thinking. Whereas for me it is the opposite.

Epicurus sat down, gesturing for Zeno the Stoic to take the floor.

'The gods seem mischievous, certainly,' he continued. 'Often capricious and out of sorts. In a single stroke they kill a man, or sink a ship. Or that is what the peasants tell us. But for a man to live well, he must realise his nature. And it is not "happiness" whatever that is, but the God given spark inside that gives us equanimity, or at least peace of mind. When we're well trained, and self-controlled, then whatever befalls us – tragedy or joy – we greet them both as imposters that can neither harm nor do us good. We all have the Logos within us.'

'Just another path to happiness,' volunteered someone in the crowd. 'Just what Epicurus is saying, but by a different path.'

'Not happiness but dignity!' replied Zeno.

'And without dignity you Stoics cannot be happy, so happiness *is* your goal,' insisted the man.

'No, it is much more aligned to virtue,' replied Zeno.

Dianthe stood without a word, bowed courteously and left them there in the garden. She had heard enough for one day. But she was glad she had come. The sun was rising in a cloudless sky and the day was all before her. She wanted to think of Aristippus, she wanted to experience the wound. She wanted to wonder – now she was grown – whether what he had said could be true. The thought of his actions had brought it all back – the anger and the hurt. No amount of philosophy, sitting in a garden could begin to take it away. Their words were suddenly senseless. But, still, she was glad she had come.

* * * * * * * *

'Well! That was instructive,' said Chesterton sarcastically, fishing out the volume still in his shoe. The wind had organised a place that was sheltered, though she still hung around as if brooding. 'That says it all!' the journalist continued. 'That was as disgusting, as it was wrong!'

Nietzsche said nothing, but stared into the distance being still caught up in the scene. Eventually he turned, his face straining with some kind of emotion.

'That's where I have my roots,' he said finally. 'All that the fellow was saying, is what I have said nearly two and a half thousand years in his future! He was an Übermensch!'

'Will you explain, once and for all, what you mean by this Übermensch thing?' Chesterton had much more to say on the story, but he wanted to clear up this word. He replaced the book on his ample knee and patted it distractedly.

'A thing unique and *Beyond Good and Evil* (the title of one of my books). Your insipid English of course, cannot reach it but it means something like this; a man higher than everyone else because he alone is unafraid. He doesn't care for convention but forges his life for himself. "And so onwards," I wrote, "Be your own source of experience. Forgive yourself your own self. And then your life will be yours."

Chesterton considered. The wind played in the pine trees, creating sudden, surprising gusts. The two men listened to her for a while and before long a bird could be heard.

'You do not comment?' said Nietzsche at last. 'Have I to

assume I've convinced you then? In all that I say about boldness?'

'It's extremely modern,' replied the other, feeling his way towards what he wanted to say. 'But it doesn't address the issue. There are some things that are wrong however you see them. Where the evil is beyond any convention. I could agree that a man must be free, but not so free as to abuse a child. A man cannot be his own source of experience when that experience damages others.'

'There are no absolute rules – just the judgement of the age and time!' replied the philosopher coldly.

'And the judgment of the Ancient Greeks allowed slavery and tolerated a scene such as that! But can't we – from our different perspective – find a way to say that it's wrong? Basic human rights were destroyed in that story – the children were wrongly abused. People should be respected – regardless of age or status. Can't we from our perspective – find something to say about that?'

'I doubt it. From where would you get such perspective – other than Kant?' And Nietzsche gesticulated at the train of Sages. 'Or Aquinas!' he added, equally dismissively.

Chesterton raised his hands and looked like he could hit him. 'It's obvious, man!' he said, as the colour came to his face. 'Some things are instinctively wrong – you know it and I do! It goes against nature – the hideousness of abuse. It destroys the idea of protection, quite apart from destroying a life. It *feels* repugnant. There is not very much to debate!'

Nietzsche spat contemptuously and rammed a twig into the ground, twisting it round with a vengeance. 'Who....do you think....is watching?'

'Quite apart from whether anyone is "watching,"' replied his companion with equanimity, 'by whom I assume you mean God, there are questions about this notion of pleasure. That child in the story was young – too young. She and the boys were simply abused.'

Nietzsche ground the stick into the ground so fiercely that it gave way and snapped.

'It is brave to know your own pleasure,' he said. 'For that is what the warrior does. To hell with the custom of the age. For that is what you talk of – just custom! There is no absolute rule and the child that appears too young – to you – was not too young for the Greeks. People are not so.... so *uniform* and nothing is permanently true,' and he ground the stub of the stick down harder, pleased with his apt choice of words. 'I agree that relations with a child are unnatural. But where childhood ends is a decision for the state. Different countries have different ideas! People in the past were married at twelve and even today there is no common age. It is absurd to claim an absolute – when sane people cannot agree!'

'Sane people all say that abuse is wrong!' retorted the journalist, with equal vehemence. 'Though they may differ over when it occurs. But the understanding runs deep inside us. It's to what we always return!'

The discussion infuriated Nietzsche. 'Morality is not a herd instinct!' he snarled, turning angrily to grab another stick. 'There is no such thing as a human nature that can routinely condemn or defend. What is wrong for you – or many – may not be wrong for me. It is that, I am arguing about.' And he ground the stick so fiercely that it, also, gave way and snapped.

'It revolts me,' said Chesterton simply.

'Bah!'

'I keep returning to the earlier scene – to the monk,

Thomas Aquinas. He would have said there's a reason for that revulsion. That it goes against our nature.'

'His nature was very small,' spat the German. 'I would not share a nature like his – caught up in some quest for God! His life was the poorer for it. God is dead – you know that!'

Chesterton leant back, plucked a piece of grass, stuck it in his mouth and chewed it. He was beginning to regain his composure. And he had had an idea.

'There are things that remain always wrong – whatever the age. And others that go with the time.'

'And who says this?' hissed Nietzsche, who was far from giving up yet. 'Other than some kind of God? The only guide can be man!'

'All right,' said the journalist, uncrossing his legs and turning to face his opponent. 'Let's do as you say and take God away. Ditch his commandments and look for some other source of good that spans the centuries and that everyone wants. You would agree – I believe – that happiness matters?'

Nietzsche frowned and did not reply.

'The pursuit of happiness may well be worthwhile,' continued the journalist, warming to his theme, 'But leagues apart from what we've just seen.'

'Related!' growled his opponent.

Chesterton ignored him; conceding the point. There is a school – a respectable school – going back to Epicurus, that does talk of human pleasure as being a very great good. Not the rapturous pleasure of the selfish man. But the pleasure of doing one's best.' He opened the book and turned to the index, running his finger through the names.

'You cannot take me to another of my enemies so early in our journey! Why would I visit the blockhead Mill? He lived at the time I was alive! Can't we stay there in the distant past?' Nietzsche's anxiety was almost comical to see. He had realised straight away where they were going.

'Not if we're talking about pleasure,' said Chesterton, finding the page and opening the book to lie flat. 'Because that's what you're ultimately asserting. That pleasure is the guide to our life.'

Nietzsche shook his head and leapt to his feet, attempting to snatch the small volume. And failing to do so.

'This is not pleasure this Mill! This is not pleasure like the Greek! It is not making them happy – it has nothing to do with excess!'

'Excess?'

'Yes! Yes' screamed Nietzsche. 'And how good is this pleasure he values? How high or low it is? How like virtue can he make it!' He spat at the word with contempt. 'Who is he, to judge *that*?'

'I would have said John Stuart Mill had a claim.'

'*Nein! Nein!*'

'Well. Good heavens man! You can still see him over there. And his story looks inviting.'

'It is not pleasure,' hissed the German frantically. 'It is not pleasure this thing! It is corrupt this pleasure! It only pretends to be fine. It is not brave or noble or true!'

Chesterton chuckled good naturedly as he prepared to view Mill's story.

'No, no my dear fellow. It is my turn. And I see there's a female character. How jolly! I knew there was something missing. Very good! Very good indeed! Another female perspective!'

* * * * * * * *

59

AVIGNON 1873

John Stuart Mill

The garden gate is open and a short pathway leads to the house. A young girl, about seventeen, hesitates, eyeing the open window for signs of life inside. The bright sunlight blinds her and the room beyond is dark, so she doesn't see him watching her. Then the upstairs casement flies open and a woman hangs out, waving her hand in a single, abrupt signal.

'Don't just stand there, Evangeline. Come in!'

The confusion once she is over the threshold is no better. She can't just linger, like an idiot, in the hall. Should she go into the room to the left or the right? Which is her teacher's study? Both doors are closed. She hesitates for just a fraction too long and then watches in dismay as one swings open. 'Whatever else, do not disturb my stepfather,' Miss Taylor had warned her. 'He must work and will not take kindly to noise or bother.' And now she has done precisely that. Disturbed him.

She has just time for her hand to fly to her bonnet before he stands in front of her. A lean man, slightly stooped, with heavy sideburns and thin, unsmiling lips. She is immediately terrified.

'Can I help you?'

'I'm so sorry to bother you, sir,' she says. 'I am Evangeline Haverton, Miss Taylor's pupil. My lesson begins at three.'

'An actress?' he enquires, with a hint of surprise.

'Only in my dreams!' The answer seems to strike him because he looks slightly less forbidding and shows her into Helen Taylor's room, holding the door with impeccable manners and standing back to let her pass.

It's a cheerful little room, entirely devoid of the heavy English furniture so many people bring with them to France. Her own parents could be accused of having transposed one house for another. When she's at home in Avignon, she could equally well have been in London, were it not for the probing sun. This house is quite different. Unusual really, with white painted furniture and pretty blue curtains that let in light and ease.

When her teacher, Miss Taylor, comes in, her appearance contrasts with the cheerfulness of the room. She seems the female equivalent of her stepfather, uptight and strict, despite her reputation as an actress. Evangeline, bursting with the flighty novels she's read, wants her teacher to be theatrical and vague. Miss Taylor is all buttoned up.

'Forgive me, Father. I won't permit her to disturb you,' the woman remarks, as if Evangeline might sting. But the austere gentleman could not be more charming.

'Nonsense, Helen. How could a young person daring to be different be anything but delightful to me? Are you the first actress in your family?'

'A great trouble to my parents, I'm afraid, sir.'

'Excellent. I like anyone who offers a challenge.'

And that is their first exchange.

Helen Taylor glances at her pupil, assessing her coldly now they are on their own. 'We shall read from Hamlet,' she says. 'You may play the prince, and I'll be everyone else.'

Evangeline begins to read. She is a tentative Hamlet, more

afraid of her black satined teacher than the ghost or the king combined. Miss Taylor, by contrast, is loosening up. She swoons dramatically as Ophelia, plays a ponderous Polonius and is an indignant ghost. With each new part she gradually divests herself of clothing. First the shawl, then the trim grey jacket and then the dress collar are thrown to the floor. She is positively denuded by the time the Prince is facing his mother.

'Now, hate me!' she hisses at Evangeline. 'Despise me for what I have done. Imagine me desporting with your uncle!'

Evangeline tries not to laugh. She is not shocked. Her liberal upbringing has equipped her well. Despite her nerves she is enjoying the exchange, beginning to warm to the strait-laced eccentric, bouncing on the divan in front of her.

'Oh, Hamlet, speak no more! Thou turn'st mine eyes into my very soul,' Miss Taylor is egging her on.

'Nay but to live in the rank sweat of an enseaméd bed, stewed in corruption, honeying and making love over the nasty sty.' Evangeline doesn't blush. By the window the piano stands uncovered, proudly displaying its legs. She likes its honesty. She is starting to like this house.

By the time she has died – rather languidly in Horatio's arms – she is quite relaxed and excited. Horatio is a friend. She is used to his warm approval. She doesn't like it when Fortinbras takes over, and Miss Taylor's voice grows hard and unfamiliar again. Then the play ends and the energy hangs like ectoplasm between them; the ghost of what they've just done.

'You will stay to tea?' Miss Taylor is flushed, awake. Still strict but no longer frightening.

'I would love to. That was amazing,' she says, rising to her feet as the older woman gets to hers. 'I learned so much, just from the way you played the different parts.'

Miss Taylor allows herself a brief smile. 'Stay here while I fetch the tray. My stepfather might join us.'

It is Mr Mill who carries in the tea tray. Evangeline is surprised. Her own father wouldn't do that.

'You have enjoyed yourself?' he enquires, without the expected "my dear".

'It was wonderful,' she says, still awash with excitement. 'I learned so much.' If she blushes now it's because she is repeating herself. Her mother says the man's a genius.

'Do you think happiness comes through learning?' he is almost playful, pouring the tea as if he is accustomed to do it.

Evangeline is demure. 'Certainly, sir,' she says, balancing her tea cup, hoping her hand doesn't shake.

As soon as she thinks about it, the hand starts to tremble. The china rattles; the hand has a mind of its own. It's infuriating as she's not even nervous any more. And now she looks like she is.

'I think happiness is what it's all about, especially trying to do what you really want to do. I have wanted to be an actress since a very small child.' The long sentence is some recompense for the stupid hand which, at last, begins to behave. 'Thank you,' she says, taking the shortbread with poise, to show them she's back in control.

John Stuart Mill doesn't hurry to fill the gap.

'I'm glad you don't want to be like everyone else,' he says finally. 'It's a good thing to be different. There's a significant evil in following the crowd, for crowds tend to be stupid and incapable of independent thought.'

The approval emboldens Evangeline. She glances at Miss Taylor who looks back. He sees the look.

'My stepdaughter is a very great actress, but she has

given it all up to look after me. I tell her it's an ignoble sacrifice, but she has a mind of her own. In that she is not unlike her mother.'

Evangeline knows she's standing on the edge of scandal.

Mill is continuing, 'You know my late wife – Miss Taylor's mother – is buried here in France?'

'I do, sir. My parents tell me you visit the grave every day.'

'She was a very fine woman. Incomparable. And now I have another very fine woman to assist me in my thinking.' He smiles kindly at his stepdaughter who repays him, modestly, with her own.

'Evangeline played a very passing Hamlet,' she says. 'Though she needs to work on her pacing. We all speak more quickly when impassioned.'

'Indeed,' he says. 'I remember getting through my work at India House very quickly in order to give myself time for greater things. Efficiency, perhaps, is the key.'

'And on that note,' he says, rising and gesturing to the ladies to remain seated, 'I must return to the greater things. We will see you again, Evangeline?'

She is startled by the use of her Christian name. 'I do hope so, sir,' she says, returning his gaze with a clear, bold look. 'That is if Miss Taylor…'

'You may call me Helen.' It is more of a command than anything else.

* * *

Her mother is languorously beautiful, swaying in the hammock with a glass of cordial. She is reading. Not for the first time Evangeline wonders how she manages to remain so perfectly white. She, herself, would only have to look at the swinging net to attract green stains to her blouse, but her mother is effortlessly graceful.

She looks up from her book. 'Hello darling. You're back soon. How was it? Was Miss Taylor terrifying?'

'Only at first.' She throws herself down on the chequered rug, kicks off her shoes and hitches her skirt to enjoy her new white stockings.

'Don't let the gardener see you,' her mother warns vaguely, lowering her head to read. But Evangeline is not ready to let her go.

'I met him.'

'Who darling?'

'Mr Mill of course. The man who father calls the "greatest and most dangerous mind in England". He didn't seem so risky to me.'

'Good,' says her mother abstractedly, stretching her arms up to embrace the sky.

'He mentioned his wife.'

'The renowned Harriet Taylor,' her mother puts down her book and shields her eyes against the five o'clock sun. 'When I was growing up, their relationship was quite the scandal of Westminster.'

'But he was so unscandalous,' she says, thinking of the tall, prim man.

Her mother turns to prop herself up on one arm. 'Everyone ages, darling. And he did marry her in the end.'

Evangeline is fascinated. 'So what was the scandal?' she asks, hoping her mother will continue and not get suddenly bored and resume her reading. But her mother is ready to play.

'Harriet Taylor was the wife of John Taylor, a pharmacist, a "dull good man", someone once said. She was a society hostess in a small way. Fond of being seen as a radical intellectual though she was good looking, and it's normally only plain women who bother to make themselves clever.'

Evangeline smiles, pleased with how they both snub the rule.

'Harriet Taylor invited Mill to a dinner and was immediately attracted to him. He was very brilliant and rather sad. He'd had a fierce upbringing, so people say. Harriet herself had a neck like a swan and was fond of saying surprising things, according to Jane Carlyle. She entrapped him. Within a year they were appearing together at parties. It was the talk of the town. Absolutely scandalous. I thought it very bold!'

'What about the husband, Mr Taylor?'

'Well exactly.' Her mother pauses dramatically. She knows where her daughter gets it from. 'The husband was too dull – or brave – to seek a divorce. He allowed Mill to come to the house three times a week to entertain jointly with Harriet, and on those evenings he would go to his club. People used to say that Mill was at their house so much he paid to restock the cellar. What's more, Taylor brought Harriet a place out of London, in the country, which he visited once a month. Most other weekends Mill was there, though it was very hushed up at the time. And they used to travel together, all over the place. I remember talk about someone meeting them in Switzerland, going about freely, she holding onto his arm.'

'But he seems such a sweet old gentleman.'

'Who says he can't be?' Evangeline's mother is radical enough in her own way and the heat of the Provencal sun uplifts her. 'When the good Mr Taylor at last saw fit to die, it took two years for Mill to marry his wife. Maybe he was in no rush because the contract would give them nothing they'd not already enjoyed. Are you going back to his stepdaughter?'

'Can I? Will father fund it?'

'You can fund it yourself from your allowance,' her mother smiles, reaching again for her book. 'If that's how you wish to spend money.'

'I want to be an actress. I'll do whatever it takes, and Miss Taylor is the only person, certainly the only English person, who offers acting lessons in Avignon. When we get back to London I might find someone else. But until then...' Evangeline lies down on the rug and studies the shadows of the Eucalyptus tree, dreaming of treading the boards in a flea pit or the Garrick. She unbuttons her chemise and allows the sun to kiss her neck, heedless of her mother's warning. Before long she is asleep. Half a mile away, John Stuart Mill puts down his pen, reads through the pages he has been writing and stacks the sheets together in an orderly fashion. Then he gets up and goes into the herbarium. He wants to do some botany.

* * *

The tricycle is heavy and the potted fern she has bought is heavier still, drooping over its tub in a lopsided sulk. She wishes she had left them both at home. It's impossible to ride and keep the plant upright in the basket, so she ends up pushing the thing all the way up the cobbled street. The locals eye her struggle with amusement.

It's Mill himself who answers the door. He peers round as if puzzled.

'How very nice to meet you,' he says.

'Sir, it's me, Evangeline,' her face is partly covered by a fern leaf.

'I know,' he says, without smiling, 'I was addressing *hemionitis arifolia*.' He takes it from her and disappears, thanking her politely. She checks her purse and waits. She has the guinea ready. For some reason, the English stick to their own currency when dealing with each other abroad. She waits five minutes, ten. The hallway is cool but there is nowhere to sit, so she shifts from one foot to another and hopes Miss Taylor will come.

There is a movement and she straightens her back, but it is merely a fat tabby who eyes her carelessly and pads across the hall, before jumping through a window at the back. The morning breathes on; time measured by the steady tick of the clock mounted on one of the walls.

After twenty slow minutes have passed, she thinks she should slip away. But then, how awful if Miss Taylor is merely late. How rude she will seem to leave! Could she have forgotten? Has she got the day wrong? Something is clearly amiss. Another ten minutes and she is really prepared to go. But her sense of fair play intervenes. After all, they definitely had made an appointment. She knocks at the door through which Mill's disappeared. He answers immediately.

'Come in.'

'I had an appointment this morning, sir. My second lesson, but Miss Taylor…'

'Miss Taylor has gone into town,' he pushes the chair back, which grates against the uneven stone of the cottage floor. 'She took the dog-cart this morning, and I fear we didn't speak, bar pleasantries. I imagine she must have forgotten, unless, of course, you are wrong?'

Evangeline holds her ground, 'No, sir. I am certain it is today. I have been looking forward to it all week. It's why I bought the plant,' she adds needlessly.

Mill is looking down at the thick sheaf of papers covered with his small, neat writing. Heaped on his desk are books lying open; annotated, underlined, scored in the margin. It's a world of ideas in the space of six feet.

'I could teach you,' he says, from out of the blue.

'Acting, sir?' Evangeline doesn't know what else to say.

Mill looks annoyed and Evangeline wants to swallow the words. She is standing in the presence of England's greatest living philosopher; thrown together in a cottage five hundred miles from home, and she is not grateful or charming but flippant. Even though she has no interest in philosophy, he would make a rich character study. Some things just have to be grabbed.

'I'm sorry,' she stammers. 'I didn't... It's just that I'm so stupid, sir. I don't know anything about philosophy or clever, bookish things. I'm just a girl.'

'Please don't say that in this house! No one should say "just a girl" unless you want to be compared unfavourably to a man. You must stand up for your sex!'

Evangeline is not used to being reprimanded, especially for such a trifle. She tilts her head back and answers with as much composure as she can.

'If I meant anything, I was comparing my youth and my anonymity with your career, sir. I meant I am just a girl; one girl, any girl, standing in the presence of something of which I know nothing but about which I'd like to know more.' The last bit is a lie, for politeness.

Mill softens. He does like this young person with her wide awake face and her backbone when confronted. He remembers what it feels like to be young and in awe and to have a hand that shook when you least wished it.

'I can teach you here or in the garden. I expect you to

take no notes for these are not my published views, just the ramblings of experience when confronted afresh with youth. You will not broadcast what I say?'

Evangeline shakes her head, wondering how to escape.

'Might we sit in the garden then? I am hopeless in resisting the sun!' Her precious guinea clinks in its flimsy purse and she suppresses her dismay. Under the current, surprising arrangement, she's not sure that money is even appropriate. She takes comfort in the thought that her father will be able to advise her; the luxurious fall-back, known by every sheltered and secure young thing, of having a parent who will pay. She steps out of the wide French doors. The tabby jumps up and kneads Mill's bony lap while Evangeline fetches an ironwork chair and joins him under the parasol.

'So now, where to begin?' he laces his fingers together and cracks them, saying nothing. Eventually he selects a mental pathway and raises his stern, grey eyes.

'You said that you think happiness is "what it's all about". A good sentiment and one that I share, despite appearances to the contrary,' he adds, and Evangeline is not sure whether he's joking. She smiles politely and wonders how long it will take.

'I think the best thing is to start at first principles.' She doesn't like that word. She doesn't really know what it means. He sees her look and continues.

'Take this insect here, scuttling back and forth between the flower pot and my shoe. If I raise my foot to crush it, what do you think it will do?'

'Run away if it sees the danger.'

'And why? Why will it run?'

'Because it has no wish to be squashed, sir!'

'What would it feel if it was "squashed," as you put it?'

'Pain and subsequently death, I suppose.'

He chuckles dryly. 'Leaving aside the problem of whether anything *feels* death, what mental state would it experience having escaped my upturned foot?'

'Probably relief!' She doesn't know if she's on the right track at all.

'What does Puss here feel, at ease with the world on my knee?'

'She seems to be enjoying it, sir.'

'And what do you feel when you are doing something you really enjoy? Reading Hamlet for example.'

'I feel pleasure, sir. Happiness.' Evangeline understands. 'You're suggesting that the cat, the insect and I, all have happiness in common?' Philosophy is easier than she thought.

'I'm suggesting, as the Ancient Epicureans did, that every creature lives its life seeking pleasure and avoiding pain. As Jeremy Bentham said, "Nature has placed mankind under the governance of two sovereign masters, pleasure and pain." You feel much greater pleasure than the beetle or the cat, but nevertheless all three of you have pleasure as your starting point.'

'And the meaning of life is the pursuit of pleasure?' Evangeline is discomforted, she had thought there was more to it than that!

'What of virtue, of Christian duty, of charity, sir? Pleasure sounds too selfish and self-serving to be noble. It also sounds too quick!'

'I'm not, initially speaking, of what is noble, just of what is true. Your most selfless – or apparently selfless – action has at its heart the pursuit of pleasure. But I am running on.' He smiles for the first time, and she glimpses a pool of kindness. 'Maybe it is easiest if I tell you something of my

71

own life and perhaps, by discussion, you will see where the philosophy leads.'

He settles himself more comfortably, puts the cat down, crosses his thin tweed legs and asks, 'Was your childhood happy?'

Why don't the normal social barriers exist for him? What right does he have to know?

'Good. I ask because mine was not. My father was a utilitarian, a follower of Bentham who first set down this great system which acknowledges that the world seeks – and ought to seek – the pursuit of pleasure and the avoidance of pain. Bentham was enraged by the poverty he witnessed and saw his life's work as increasing the sum of human happiness. The pleasure of the majority, he concluded, must be of more importance than that of the minority. He was logical; if happiness is what everyone wants, then the largest number of people should obtain it. "The greatest pleasure for the greatest number," he called it. My father saw his three year old son as being part of the plan.'

Evangeline notices that Mill develops a twitch above his eye. It is fascinating and has the effect of making him more vulnerable. It is also potentially amusing; she needs something to keep her awake.

'I was what's known as a "clean slate",' he continues, 'A flawless starting point in the quest to fashion a person who would be useful. Useful in what, you might ask? Useful in providing happiness to the greatest number of people. Now, to someone like you, I might uncharitably guess, happiness is a serious business that has much to do with lying in the sun or playing tennis or taking the boat out on the lake. Am I right? Whereas, to my father, happiness meant creating an educated child who could be useful in promoting his

Benthamite ideal. By the age of three, I was not only reading Greek but writing my own shaky sentences. It was taken for granted that my father's own capacity for work would be mine as well, and our days were spent on either side of a table while he wrote and I studied. There was no dictionary other than the most rudimentary grammar, so whenever I was "stuck", as you would put it, I had no recourse than either to work out the problem for myself or be bold enough to disturb my father, which I had not much appetite to do. So, by dint of habit, I learned to think for myself, to test my assumptions, to see things from every angle and assume that every solution has an error that will invite you to start again. When the errors stop, truth starts.'

'That must have been terrible, sir,' she says, thinking that he undoubtedly intends to teach her in the same monumentally tedious way.

'So let's think a little more about Bentham's system of utility. He was a remarkable man, I should add; long, flowing hair and a walking stick called Dapple. Set up University College in London and gave his body to science and, when science had finished with it, to the students so they could play football with his head. Now, what Bentham realised was, if it were true that everyone wants pleasure, then the vast majority of people are the losers because all the money and all the power lies in the hands of a very few; a minority, who rule us and do everything they can to keep the majority down. As I've said, Bentham campaigned for the working man and the poor. They should have pleasure too. Do you agree, Evangeline?'

She considers carefully before replying,

'But isn't it difficult to lump pleasures together like that, sir? I mean, what are the poor man's pleasures? My father tells me they spend a lot of time drinking spirits.'

'Whereas, he prefers to lay down a cellar of wine? Yes, we'll come to that later. For the moment let's just concentrate on Bentham's assessment of pleasure. The most important thing you have to take in, is that for Bentham all pleasure is equal. It doesn't matter that you might like Shakespeare, while another might like to get drunk. There's essentially no difference between the merits of the two activities because it's just what different people find pleasurable. Or, as he put it, "pushpin is equal to poetry." Other things about the pleasure may vary – how long it lasts, how likely it is to give birth to more happiness and so forth. But these differences are incidental. Pleasure for Bentham was a kind of pile; the highest stack wins. The bricks in the stack are the same; it's just that some towers are higher or wider than others, and the tallest or widest wins. Do you understand?'

Evangeline nods. The sun is making her drowsy. She can't really see why any of this might matter. She wishes Miss Taylor would come.

* * *

On her way home, bumping her way down the street on the tricycle, she catches herself feeling happy. Poor old Mr Mill, with his twitching eye and his earnest expression. He didn't seem to have the exploding sense of joy that she has at the sight of green pine trees against a blue sky. What was he saying about pleasure? How everyone seeks it. Well that makes sense. She halts to watch the vineyard – people tending the vines – and for the first time wonders if they are also striving for happiness. She has met Jacques Coursot, the Duc d'Avignon, who owns the land of the area. He has it easy; sitting on his terrace and instructing his manager for ten minutes a day while the rest of his life is spent with horses and backgammon. Not for the first time, Evangeline pits her own adored father against the rest of the world. How does he compare with a Mill or a Duc? How does he pursue pleasure?

'I'm home!' she shouts to no one in particular, as she flings down her parasol and pours herself a drink. They have no servants in Avignon, other than the gardener and Marie who does the cooking, and who comes up from the village in time to prepare the meals. Not like London where there are parlour maids, a cook and a coachman. 'Is anyone here?'

Her mother will be resting, she supposes, lying upstairs on her bed, or outside in the hammock. Evangeline is hazy about how these things work, but she knows enough to be surprised that her mother is going to have a baby. 'But do you want another child?' she had asked, astonished, when the announcement had come between the roast lamb and Eve's pudding.

Her mother had laughed and glanced over to her father who was deeply involved in the Gazette. 'Of course I do, darling. What a thing to ask. Won't it be lovely for you to have a brother or a sister to play with?'

'Play with!' Evangeline had snorted in distaste. 'I'm seventeen. I'm hardly going to find much amusement in crawling about on the floor!'

But against all odds, her mother's pregnancy brought its benefits. If it was possible, she was even happier than before; floating about, arranging everything. And she sang all the time. Evangeline loved to hear the soft, sweet voice floating up from the dining room as she arranged a spray of roses.

Her father, too, seemed content in his distant-close way, but whether he had moved a notch on his personal happiness barometer, Evangeline really couldn't say. He worked in Paris during the week, returning on the five o'clock sleeper every Friday night. He never brought her anything; not like the fathers of Simone and Therese who never failed to bring home chocolates or lace. Arthur brought only the smell of the linen jacket that he changed into as soon as he was home. This shabby affair, that he'd lived in as long as she could remember, heralded the start of the weekend. Its shabbiness meant picnics and boating on the lake and flying the kite on the hillside. It meant him listening from the deckchair as she read her lines; it meant the privilege of having him around.

'Mama!'

From the bottom of the garden, her mother's voice locates her presence.

'Have you fed Bijoux?'

There is no answer, so Evangeline goes to the pantry, lifts the lid off the milk churn and ladles out a cupful. Then she takes a large syringe, of the type they use in *l'hôpital,* and draws off as much as she can.

Sally, the black Labrador, who like most things has been with them almost as long as she can remember, will be outside in the shade; her fat puppies pummelling each other in their funny, grunting efforts to get to the best teat. Only little Bijoux will be left out. 'The runt', her father calls him, saying he should 'go to a better place.' Even his own mother seems to regard him with disdain, refusing to clean him and purposefully getting up when he finally reaches her milk. He is a victim of one. A minority; were it not for his powerful ally who feeds him five times a day and twice during the night.

She finds him lying on his own, while the other puppies snooze in a twitching, smooth-haired, puppy mountain.

'Come on, Bijoux. Lunch time!' Evangeline knows that

without her, Bijoux wouldn't have survived, and his enthusiasm for life remains tenuous. He's getting stronger though. With her unfailing sense of fair play, Evangeline defends the victim. When she was a child in Elementary, before the dreaded governess, she'd been the underdog, teased for being a "Frenchie". She knows what it feels like to be marginalised, to have her "friends" go quiet when she wants to join in and play. She has always been suspicious of groups. She has come a long way since then but not so far as to have forgotten. Her instinct still lies with minorities.

Bijoux, fed and cuddled, she places him in the middle of the puppy pile, and within seconds a boisterous male bites him on the ear. Bijoux yelps but Evangeline lets him be. As he gets stronger he will have to fight his own battles and take his chances among the ruck. She'll keep him though, so he'll be the winner in the end, staying at home when all the others are given away.

She wanders past the tennis court in search of her mother. Patrice, the gardener, has mown the lawns and the smell of cut grass brings a little corner of England to Southern France. In other gardens near them, bougainvillea and hibiscus run riot; here there are lupins and roses.

'Do you feel well, Mama?'

'Blissful, now the sickness has passed.' With her seventeen year old energy, it seems to Evangeline that her mother's charmed existence is indolent and underspent; a lifetime of pottering and resting from pottering. She wishes she would *do* something. 'If you just pass me up your book, I can hear your lines.'

Evangeline ignores her.

'Do you remember that time at the lake, Mama?'

It's her mother's turn to disregard the question. 'Have you learned them?'

But Evangeline is insistent.

'Do you remember that time on the lake? There's something I've never understood. Did Daddy know you couldn't swim?'

'I was fine. I clung to the boat.'

The intervening years have never really erased it for Evangeline. Never fully absorbed the panic of the infamous "boating incident". She supposes every family must have such an event and, rather like getting back on a horse, they took the boat out again the next day. She has no idea how or why the boat tipped over, but what she does remember is the sudden, gasping cold and her petticoat wrapped around her shoulders, preventing her from moving as she starts to sink. More vaguely, she remembers the giant water lilies above her, blocking out the sun and the shock of not being able to breathe. And then light again, and a great draught of air, and the sensation of being pulled quickly, on her back. And from somewhere far away, the screams of a woman drowning.

Her father had made a choice; that was the truth of it. He had saved her, his child, before the woman, his wife. He had got her to the bank, gasping and half drowned, before going back to save her mother and, in that choice, lay the secret of Evangeline's guilt-tipped strength. She doesn't envy him the decision, doesn't even know if it was rational. Just the grip of instinct when faced with imminent threat. You could say it was his only option and her mother had more of a chance. But the mechanics of it, the split-second assessment, has always worried her and the talk with Mill has brought it back. If she's understood today correctly, her father's decision was based on an assessment of pleasure; which life would bring him the most.

'Mr Mill is a strange old man,' she remarks to change the conversation she herself started. 'On two counts. Firstly, he wants to teach me, and secondly he thinks everything can be reduced to pleasure.'

'Your grandfather would have something to say about that!' Evangeline's grandfather is the Bishop of London. 'They've clashed over some of the reforms Mr Mill is trying to press through, and the freedom of the press. I hope we're wise letting you go to that household. If Daddy is right, Mill not only supports Darwin but shores up working men's rights and campaigns for females too. I hope you're not going to turn into one of those awful, strident women who find it insulting when a man gives up his seat on the omnibus!'

'I won't, Mama. But he's truly a bit of a poppet. He taught me today. Not acting of course. He called it philosophy, but I think he was actually lonely and wanted someone to talk to. I'll go back again. I find him rather fascinating in a curious, old-bone sort of way. It is funny hearing him talk about pleasure, which to me means sorbet and ice cream, when I know he means something quite different.' She stretches in the sun, watching the puppies play on the lawn. 'What's that you're reading?'

'Nothing, darling.'

'Yes it is! It's a letter. Oh, do tell! Who's writing to us now. Is it Aunt Maud saying she's coming over with the cousins? Oh please, please, please!'

But Evangeline's mother folds the letter hastily and puts it back in its envelope, where it's swallowed as an improvised marker. As it disappears between the books' pages, her daughter has just time to read 'Artur Haverton' and her father's Parisian address, written in smudgy blue ink. It strikes her as strange that anyone, other than her father, should be reading his private correspondence, but her mother's face remains perfectly composed. Nothing is given away.

'Now, how about those lines. Isn't the competition soon?'

With a sigh, Evangeline passes the script and forces herself to remember. Normally she loves this long, unfolding soliloquy revealing her character's soul. But today she's suddenly assailed with the thought, no, the conviction, that it's her mother, and not herself, who is acting. Kate's beautiful face gives nothing away. Her bell-bright words sound shallow, as if they're hiding more than they reveal. With sudden urgency, Evangeline longs for it to be the morning, when the birds wake her with the knowledge that her father is home. He has let himself in, sometime during the night, and tiptoed about so as not to disturb them. And Saturday will begin again.

* * *

'So you arranged it?' They are in the potting shed and her father has just sprinkled the lily bulbs with compost.

'No, I raised it as a possibility.'

'But why, Daddy? You know I love acting. I've not the slightest interest in philosophy and all Mr Mill wants to do is to tell me the story of his life!'

Her father seems needlessly irritated. 'If nothing else, your ability to come out with sentiments like that reassures me of the necessity! John Stuart Mill is not a teacher, Evangeline. He is not like your governess. He's not even a professor at one of the great universities which, by the way, are closed to you as a female, even if you wanted to attend.

He's above all those posts! In a hundred years, if there's one man who will stand out in this mediocre generation of ours, it will be that man. We have the honour of being his neighbours, and you have the honour of listening, carefully, to anything at all he might say. There are men and women, all over England, who would give a fortune to be in your position and have this level of access.' He turns away and Evangeline is crestfallen. Her father seems older today, grumpier. Even the linen jacket hangs dejectedly on the back of a chair. It's as if it, too, is out of favour.

'I'm not saying he's not sweet,' she says, dejectedly.

'You're not asked to find him "sweet." You're not asked to find him anything. You're simply asked to respect my wishes in having him talk to you and realise that it's a very great privilege indeed. Besides, he's taking tea with us today.'

'But it's Saturday, Daddy. You're back tomorrow! Why does anyone have to spoil our one full afternoon?'

'You're acting like a spoilt child,' her father says, as petulant as she. 'This is not the kind of behaviour I expect!' and with that, he scoops up the jacket and disappears into the house.

To make it worse, she is expected to wait on them when the Mill party arrives, precisely on the stroke of four. She resents their strait-laced entrance. The black coats she hangs in the hallway make no allowance for the heat of the Provencal sun. She imagines the talk will be politics, or philosophy, or a combination of the two. In any case, it will be boring.

She's not disappointed.

Miss Taylor, it appears, only comes alive when she's acting which she's not required to do, and hence is barely more than functional. It's her lean, tense stepfather who takes centre stage, seated on the bench outside. And he opens with a broadside.

'What's your assessment of the Jamaica situation?' He's not only addressing her father. Evangeline realises that the question is aimed equally well at any one of them, and she's not a clue what he's talking about. She's pretty sure her mother will be the same.

'Impossible,' says her father, diplomatically.

'It's the worst kind of tyranny that will have one law for its own people and quite another for a subjugated race. Nothing short of barbarity. Once again the government has blood on its hands!'

'The Governor was certainly severe.'

'Severe!' Mill's eye starts to twitch. It's the only potential amusement.

'To hang four hundred men for a trumped up insurrection in which they claimed only their rights! It is more than severe – it's barbaric!'

'What's this?' Evangeline asks, cuddling Bijoux. But no one in the party hears her.

'I read in last week's *Times*,' says her mother lightly, 'that Governor Eyre was only doing his job. He was faced with a dangerous mob. Surely he should be praised? A weaker man might have endangered the entire Jamaican colony, not to mention the sugar owners. We must, after all, protect trade.' Evangeline is open-mouthed. She has never heard her mother utter a political sentiment in her life, and now she's not only talking, but appears to have an opinion. For the first time, Evangeline's formidable self-belief begins to flicker. Perhaps it's time to grow up.

Mill is aghast. It's as if Kate has uttered a profanity. 'Declare martial law for two months, burn a thousand homes, execute over four hundred men and flog six hundred more! Do you know the age of the youngest Jamaican he hanged?'

Kate is looking to her husband for support but, for once, it is not forthcoming.

'The youngest was a boy of twelve. Twelve! Now tell me, if you can, why Eyre is not a murderer who should be tried in a court like anyone else.' Evangeline is listening intently and sees that her father is too.

Her mother is prepared to disagree, politely and decorously, but nevertheless to disagree. 'Because he's not anyone else,' she replies, with composure. 'He is the Governor, entitled to do what he needs, in order to quell native unrest.'

'Had the Jamaicans done anything wrong?' Evangeline finds herself asking.

'It was an insurrection,' says her mother.

'They were requesting their basic rights,' says Mill.

'And the youngest was a boy of twelve?'

'If that,' replies the philosopher, addressing her directly as if her youth equips, rather than undermines, any thoughts she might have.

Miss Taylor nods sympathetically, 'It's a disgrace,' she mutters, but Evangeline has eyes only for the older man.

'And why isn't anyone doing anything? Daddy, you talk to the Government all the time. Why isn't this man, this Governor Eyre, called to account as Mr Mill suggests?'

'Because there is no political will to do so. The popular feeling, the feeling in the country, is that it matters little what happens to a few black people several thousand miles from home. The British Government reflects the will of the people; the people don't care, hence the Government do nothing and award the Governor with a knighthood. It's called democracy.'

Evangeline is watching as her father explains it. He seems tired, somehow. Tired and weak. She has never felt him to be either of those things before.

'My sources tell me there might be some small investigation,' he adds, lamely.

'Your sources tell you a lot of things!'

Why is there a bite in her mother's voice? Why is there distrust and resentment in that sentence? She glances with embarrassment at the guests to see if they've noticed it too, but if they have, they're perfectly discreet.

Her father shifts uncomfortably.

'Are you pleased to be out of the House, sir?' Mill has lost the seat he held briefly at the last election.

'Delighted. I can achieve much more from the sidelines. Agitate for reform in all areas, and Heaven knows we need it.'

Evangeline is used to hearing these kinds of words. But she has never before known what they meant. They've been empty, far-off words; abstract, not to do with her. For some reason it's at that tea party, on that little lawn, that they fall into place, like a blackbird locating a worm. Maybe it's the twelve year old boy she imagines, his eyes wide with terror, as the noose is put over his neck. Evangeline doesn't know many – any – black people, but her cousin is twelve. And for the first time in her life, someone else's problem becomes her own, and she realises what politics means. At the same resounding moment she also realises that without an overarching principle, politics is a blind and hopeless affair. If you're going to help, you need a *philosophy* to implement; something you believe to be true. What had Mill said? "Happiness was the first principle," so maybe political reform was about giving joy to as many people as possible! She could assent to that! She could believe that! She could want that to happen! If only it meant saving the lives of other twelve year old boys.

'Will you walk with me, sir?'

Now, it's not just her parents who are looking surprised, Miss Taylor is, too, and even Mr Mill seems taken aback.

'Evangeline!' says her mother. 'Our guests are taking their tea.'

'Not now,' he says, looking directly at her, as if there's no one else on the lawn. 'But if you wish, I can see you early on Monday. If that's all right with your parents?'

Her mother smiles politely and refills Miss Taylor's cup. Her father, on the other hand, looks like he's just been given an honour. And, at that moment, Evangeline realises why he's done it, and what it is to love someone so much that you want the best for them, even if that best is different, and startling, and takes them in a different direction to the paths you yourself have trod. Her father respects Mr Mill. He wants Evangeline to learn from him; all the things that he himself has never had the time to teach her.

* * *

Acting is ephemeral now. She can't believe she wasted all that time learning make-believe words when there's so much to be done in the world. So many lives to save! She sees herself as a priestess, riding into foreign lands, justice and mercy falling from her sword as she cuts through the lot of the privileged. Mill sees her fervour and, in a roundabout way, tells her to calm down.

'If you are to do anything, you must be serious,' he says. 'Apply serious thought and reason. Your imagination is a tool, but it's a tool that must first be instructed. It's all very well having passion – every young person should have it – but you will never be effective unless you look your opponent in the eye and think through his objections as carefully as he.'

Now that she's prepared to *think*, he can rattle through Bentham's philosophy.

'So the first principle is happiness?' she says, drawing up her former white ironwork chair. 'And utilitarianism thinks that life should be about the most number of people getting it?'

'Elegantly put!' he says. Is he teasing her? If so, she really doesn't mind.

'But, that thing you said about crowds. How crowds can sometimes be stupid? If the majority's happiness always wins, what happens when the majority is stupid? Couldn't that lead to injustice? I mean, isn't that what happened in Jamaica?'

Mill is nodding. 'Certainly, the might of the British Empire is no match for any man who wants to stand against it and, yes, you've seen precisely the problem inherent in Bentham. If pleasure is merely a quantity of otherwise equal parts, then the small but important pleasure can so easily disappear. Nay, should disappear if Bentham is right.'

'On Saturday after you had gone, Mama said "utilitarianism is a philosophy for pigs!" What does she mean by that?'

'Your mother is a clever woman,' he replies. 'I doubt very much she really thinks that, but it might be politic for her to say so. What she means, is that *if* the majority's pleasures should win, then the kind of pleasure the majority enjoys will also win. "Wine, women and song", I believe is how the music halls put it. She means utilitarianism reduces the human race to swine; good only for feasting and rutting, and there's surely more to it than that!'

'Well she's right!' cries Evangeline, thrilled with her mother's discernment.

'Of course she's right!' he laughs, 'But she's not right in stopping there. Let me tell you what life was like, for me, at your age. You'll remember my father was strict, so strict I lived much in terror. He taught me everything he could, including the thoughts of his mentor, for he was devoted to Bentham. I arranged Bentham's work for publishing, struggling to decipher his hand and thought his philosophy a more than sufficient creed. I was committed to it. And then, one day, I asked myself a question.

'"If," I said to myself, "everything you wanted came true, all the injustices redressed; pleasure for the majority, freedom and education for all, if all that happened, would you, John Stuart Mill, be happy?" And the only answer I could reach was "No". An echoing, miserable "No". It almost destroyed me. For what was I working? How could I preach the pursuit of happiness if I had no idea of the condition myself?'

Even Evangeline is aware how intimate and privileged this is.

'What did you do?'

'For two long years I might have been dead. I was in despair, empty and alone. Then I began to read again. My father and Bentham had always despised poetry. So, in the perversity of youth, that's where I started. It was Wordsworth who first gave me hope. Allowed me to glimpse a future where feelings are not useless and rejected, but held up as vital ingredients in the mix that is somebody's life.'

'And you began to see that happiness is not something that can be measured?'

It's at that moment Mill bestows on her one of those quick, unhampered grins that goes way beyond the smiles of social convention. It's a response to her response. There's nothing he admires more than someone who's prepared to try.

'Nearly,' he says, gently. 'No, I saw that happiness can still be measured, but some pleasures should simply weigh more. An enormous pile of your mother's "piggy" pleasures are as nothing compared to the more important ones. And before you ask, I would say, pleasures of the intellect, and exertion are important, the pleasure of freedom vital.'

'If you'd had a classical education, it's at this point that you would say – politely I am sure – "But Mr Mill, surely you're not being true to your creed? The pleasures you are talking of sound like Aristotle's quest for eudaimonia, or happiness that's a by-product of virtue. If," you would say, "pleasure really is pleasure then Bentham is right. One man may enjoy butter where another finds pleasure in justice, but they are different forms of the same."'

Evangeline returns his grin. She's not sure she would have thought that, but she's quite happy to be credited with it.

'And my only answer would be a weak one, and one that has recourse to nothing more solid than hunch. But I would say that anyone who has experienced both types of pleasure – the higher, active, pleasures of the mind, and the lower, more passive desires of the rascal or the dunce – wouldn't resign what he possesses more of for the complete satisfaction of all those they have in common. It is better to be a human being dissatisfied than a pig satisfied; better to be Socrates dissatisfied than a fool satisfied.'

Evangeline agrees. She's becoming a utilitarian of the Mill variety, it's true, but she can see the attraction of happiness.

'Now, perhaps, we might walk,' he says, offering her his arm. 'That's if you're prepared to walk with a philosopher!' She takes it. They make an odd couple. The tight, thin man who leans forward as he goes, and the girl dressed in white walking lightly on his arm.

'Will Miss Taylor be very angry?' she asks. He gives her a questioning look, 'Because I appear to have abandoned my acting in exchange for some time with you.'

'Miss Taylor will approve,' he says. 'I approve. You have complete freedom to dispose of your time as you see fit. As long as your actions do no harm to others, then nobody has any right to interfere with whatever you chose to do, or think, or say.'

'But what if my words cause offence?'

'Society is big enough to absorb a little offence,' he says, patting her on the arm. 'Even Avignon is big enough for that! What were you due to recite?'

'A play by Voltaire.'

'Does it mean anything to you?'

'Not really, sir, if I'm honest. I thought it did, but now, with all these thoughts in my head, I'm not sure it does anymore.'

'What if you wrote something? Your own thoughts, something you do care about. Could you put your thoughts into something fit to recite? Miss Taylor would approve of that!'

'I don't know. Could I, sir? What should I take as my theme?'

'You could take happiness,' he says, 'for it's something you seem to believe in, and I think you might find it worthwhile.'

The two figures wander off, wrapped in their thoughts,

discussing the former slave trade and religious dissent and universal suffrage. Both are earnest and engrossed.

In another part of Avignon, Evangeline's mother dabs her eyes with a lilac hankie and tells herself not to be such a fool.

In yet another part of France, the capital of the country, her father leaves his apartment en route for his newspaper empire, though he will make a detour first. He has decided to call in, gauge the situation and reassure himself that things are all right. He considers it the least he can do.

* * *

Arthur has often thought that kindness and cruelty are more closely related than is commonly assumed. For the rest of his life, though he doesn't know it yet, he will also think that his own story depends on the reading and which angle one ultimately picks.

He was thinking about his choices as he climbed the stairs, and paused for a moment to draw breath besides the mildewed window. He didn't bother to look through it; the rooftops of Paris had little attraction, especially seen through a layer of grime. He continued climbing, his legs complaining that the garret room was always further than imagined. On each landing, a new set of cheap doors announced a panopticon of lives, closed and unknowable, were it not for the sounds of poverty; the coarse, rough tones of men cooped up at home when they should be out at work, and the incessant wail of offspring.

Arthur ignored it and continued his upward ascent. He climbed swiftly and with a sense of purpose although he was in no particular hurry. By the time he got to the top floor, the light from the third floor landing had exhausted itself completely and he had to use his hands to judge where the staircase ended. But he was familiar with the curve of the wall.

Her room lay behind another cheap door, as nameless and impersonal as anything a factory could turn out. Her life, too, would have gone like that; a brief, unremarkable event that caused no stir and ended as indiscriminately as it had been lived, with not even a gravestone as a footnote, were it not for the part he played.

He put his hand to the door and pushed it a little, noting that the clasp gave immediately and was not locked. This was a surprise, for it was ten in the morning and everyone else had been up for hours.

Her room consisted of a bedstead, a washstand in the corner and nothing else. The only light came from a small pane of glass, high on the eaves of the roof which served as both wall and ceiling. It was not a window but a rectangle of light, through which the sky was more apparent than seen.

He pushed open the door, tapping lightly with a single finger to announce himself.

'*Vous etes ici?*' One of the things he always maintained was a natural reticence and politeness. He was never less than courteous, even though she was leagues beneath him on any social scale.

'Are you ill? You are still in bed.'

Mathilde raised herself on one arm, trying her best to steady herself and stop the room from spinning in the alarming way it had done throughout the night.

'I'm late! I've overslept! I must get up!' She started to reach for her outer garment from the bedstead where she had flung it the night before, but it lay in a heap on the floor.

'Could you pass me my robe?' she asked, anxious and shy,

though there were no secrets left between them. He did so silently, watching as she swung herself round on the bed and started to pull the thing on.

'You are ill,' he said again, noting her pallor and the small beads of sweat that had appeared on her forehead with the effort of attempting to dress.

'It's nothing,' she replied. 'But I am very late. I have not yet done the fires and Madame Flouris...' but Arthur never found out what Madame Flouris would have said or done because at that moment the girl cried out sharply.

'My word!'

They both looked at the rush of liquid that had appeared on the attic room floor. Arthur took charge, helping her back into bed and replacing the dress over the end of the bedstead. He was methodical in a crisis.

'You will stay here while I fetch the doctor or someone who can help,' but, as he descended the stairs he'd climbed just moments before, he reflected that a doctor was out of the question. He reached the ground floor and banged on the concierge's door.

'Madame, the servant on the top floor is unwell. She needs help, an *accoucheur*. Do you know where such a one can be found?'

The concierge was never sure how to deal with this gentleman, whom it was obvious had been intimate with the servant, but who nevertheless maintained his dignity as if it was his business alone. She had less trouble with the girl herself, making her well aware that the whole neighbourhood regarded her as a trollop, but the English man made her uneasy. He was not exactly forbidding, but he undoubtedly had money and hence deserved respect. She bustled about, then offered herself as the midwife.

No!' said Arthur, suddenly stern. 'I need a professional woman. Not you! Someone else! Go and find me one please.'

By the time the wise woman arrived, Mathilde was advanced in her pains. Arthur sat at the end of the bed; an incongruously distinguished presence in the dreary little room. From time to time, he offered words of encouragement, but the exchange was remarkably formal. The midwife had no time for him and ushered him out. This was not the domain of a man, even a wealthy Englishman.

By the time the child was born, the servant was exhausted. This was her first labour and it had been long and not without its difficulties. But as she held the infant in her arms, Mathilde took hold of a thing of the utmost worth; something to love and be loved by, even though the child was neither asked for nor legitimate. She did not know that he would become a man who saved lives from the mud of the Somme, that his daughter would be a naturalist who wrote books and drew birds, and his granddaughter an actress adored across the globe. All from a bloodstained garret bed, in the 13th Arrondissment, where the poor people lived, and an Englishman paced the pavement outside. She did not know. How could she? All she knew was that she was sore, she was tired, her baby son was crying and her future all obscure.

By the time Arthur returned to the room, everything was in order. The bed things had somehow been changed, and from nowhere a crib had appeared, in which the little one slept with one fist pressed against his mouth and his eyes closed tight against the world. Closer inspection revealed the crib to be a drawer, but it served the purpose quite adequately.

Arthur had never known what it was to feel out of place. But there, at that moment, he did. He was grateful for it, of course; grateful that he would not be needed once he'd seen them alright. But Arthur was not a man of convention. If he had been, he would not have been there at all. He had read *On Liberty*, and if he agreed with anything from that great mind of his Avignon neighbour, he agreed with the line that read thus: "To give fair play to the nature of each, it is essential that different people be allowed to live different lives." He'd taken that to heart. It was why he had returned to the girl and why he would not easily leave. It was why she would always have money and his son would be educated well. It was why he would, forever after, sacrifice ease of heart for the comfort that he was doing his best; by everyone whom he held dear. The greatest happiness for the greatest number – it could only be maintained as long as a significant portion of the number never found out – by which he meant Kate, her unborn child and the daughter he loved more than all of them; the girl called Evangeline.

* * *

The speeches are interminable in the hot September day and the town hall packed with people for the feast of St Agricola, patron saint of the fields. The workers stand in the bar washing their tonsils with drink. They are decked out in their Sunday best; greasy jackets a size too small and all pinched in at the waist. But spirits are running high.

Evangeline and her party sit patiently. They have endured lectures on the climate of the Antibes, the vascular system of cows, the might of the French railway system and now the restoration of civic pride. Monsieur Gasberre, who is shuffling his papers, has been restoring the pride for some time. His solution is not yet a universal success, for most people have fallen asleep.

Evangeline's turn comes at last. She is nervous now, seeing the Mill party all trussed up and her parents sitting there; proud and willing her on.

She gets to the table which is perched on a dais, and looks out over her audience, many of whom have left. But as people leave, others arrive, drifting in from the bar with their glasses in hand.

'I want to talk to you about happiness,' she says, in perfect French, 'and suggest that this is what life is about. I am indebted to Mr Mill who is with us today, for views that have informed my thinking.'

Evangeline pauses and looks over her audience. She imagines herself on a stage. It helps keeps the nerves at bay.

'Happiness, as Mr Mill asserts, consists of pursuing the higher pleasures over the lower ones. As examples of this, he invites us to look at two ideals which at first seem different to happiness: Justice and Liberty. He asserts that, without them, no happiness can survive and their pursuit is a higher pleasure.

'I invite you to look at this idea of his; that there are distinctions between the pleasures, and some pleasures are *worth* more than others. For, I must disagree.' She looks at Mill and to her relief sees that he is suddenly all ears – attentive and alert. Not cross as she had feared. She continues, willing her hands not to shake.

'Let us look at these lower order pleasures, like pleasures of the body,' she says. One or two men at the back start to heckle appreciatively. They had no idea the day would be such fun. Evangeline blushes but forges ahead.

'When I consider food and drink, I see that I need them both. That is my first point.

The second is this; that bodily pleasures take no practice. I don't have to be educated to enjoy them.

And thirdly, when I am deprived of these pleasures, the pain is really quite bad. I don't like it!' She looks up, unsure why people are laughing. 'And it's not as if the pain ends quickly. It stays until it's addressed.'

'So to conclude, I think the pleasures of the body are no less than those of the mind. Not really. Bodily pleasures are necessary – without them there'd be no mind!' She looks at Mr Mill who is beaming from his seat in the middle row.

The men on the back row are obviously amused, smiling into their drinks and raising their glasses.

'I'll drink to bodily pleasures!' shouts a vineyard worker, well in his cups. 'And I'll show you what they might mean!' But Evangeline doesn't hear him because her father has risen to his feet and is applauding loudly. Her mother and the Mill party join in, along with many of their neighbours, so she has no idea what the more raucous members of the audience might be shouting.

'Well done,' says Mill, walking up and extending his hand. 'Good arguments, well remembered. I will have to consider them myself.' He smiles and she knows he already has, though they had all appeared so new.

Her father is more circumspect.

'Good girl,' he says.

'Was it all right?' she asks, holding on to his arm as they leave the room together, her mother walking behind. 'Was I all right?'

'You were,' he says briefly, for her father is not prone to praise. 'You were all right.' And that is enough for Evangeline. It was all she had wanted to hear.

It's Kate's turn to pass the time of day with Mr Mill. Her husband is back in Paris and Evangeline's on a picnic with friends, so Kate is quite alone. She wanders through the village, stopping to talk to acquaintances and feeling the baby within her. She hopes against hope it will be a daughter, a little sister for Evangeline. Kate is good at raising girls; knows how to make them feel beautiful while all the while making them so.

She is planning an outfit for her unborn daughter when she meets Mr Mill, coming out of the ironmonger's in the central street of the town. He raises his hat and comes over. 'Good day, Mrs Haverton! I have been meaning to congratulate you on Evangeline's very brave speech. She is a fine young woman, the sort of woman who should one day be casting her vote. An advertisement for her sex; independent, thoughtful and bright.'

'Thank you, sir.' Kate turns her parasol and thinks about pronouncing on the weather but decides she has this opportunity just once, and she does not want to waste it.

'I rather despise your philosophy,' she says coolly. A bold statement made quite out of the blue. She doesn't care; for it's the way her thoughts have led her. 'Virtue counts far more than pleasure. Doing good is more important than being happy.'

'Madam!' Mill nods. He is civil and not in the least bit cold. He enjoys those who disagree.

'Loyalty is more important than pleasure,' she continues with perfect charm.

'Utilitarianism would agree with you.' Mill smiles and opens his hands to show the largesse of his position. 'It would say that, in nearly all cases, loyalty is good because it brings pleasure in the end.'

'But not, in itself, worth anything?'

'No, madam, only happiness is of intrinsic worth.'

'It's a philosophy without God!'

'It depends on what God might be saying,' Mr Mill smiles again. He could almost be accused of smiling suavely were he not too earnest for that. '"Do as you would be done by" sounds as if God wished his creatures to be happy.'

'But whose happiness? Should I sacrifice my happiness for that of another?' She's thinking of the Parisian girl.

'Self-sacrifice is nothing if no good comes from it. The man who fasts in the desert achieves nothing. No one benefits but his own self-worth!'

'Self-sacrifice might mean adjusting to a new situation and finding some happiness there,' she says, twirling her parasol so that her face is shielded against the sun.

'Especially if it adds to the happiness of those around us,' he says, unaware of the significance of his words.

'On that, then, we can agree. I'm so glad, Mr Mill. I wanted to find something we could agree on,' she says as lightly and decorously as only a true lady can. 'You put the end as happiness, I put it as being noble, but it amounts to quite the same thing!'

He laughs. 'You have arrived at the one criticism of my philosophy that really knocks me,' he says, as casually as she. 'That happiness is not nearly as simple as it might appear to be, and very much more like virtue than it might be comfortable for a good utilitarian like myself to uphold.'

'And on that *happy* note,' she chuckles, and holds out her hand, 'I will wish you good day, Mr Mill.'

'Good day, madam. My respects to your delightful family.'

'And to your stepdaughter, sir! Good day!'

As Kate walks up the street, twirling her parasol and picking her way through the dust, she decides on a plan. It is a plan of silence and of carrying on just as before. She loves her husband and nothing of that has changed. She loves her daughter, she will love the coming child. She desires them all to be happy. If she ever has to consider the girl in Paris again, she's sure she will be brave. It's a plan that lasts her for the rest of her life.

* * * * * * * *

They had moved; the philosopher, the journalist and the book.

They were no longer in the sunshine with pine trees and the sky. Now, they found themselves hemmed inside a busy shopping centre where people swarmed around. Plastic bags were the order of the day. That and intense, committed faces. Young people pushed, older people sank in to high-speed coffee islands, babies in buggies were whizzed about as if this was the habitat for which they'd been bred. Everyone was after the same thing: a simplified form of pleasure.

For the first time, Nietzsche and Chesterton looked at each other with something like an accord. Apart from being inside a vast plastic bubble, through which blew not a gust of fresh air, they were both bowled over by the noise. From nowhere music floated, stridently cheerful and forlorn. They found themselves standing in the doorway of a global fashion chain between a naked female mannequin and the human shoppers. The philosopher and the journalist were rooted to the spot and could have been mistaken as leery old men, were it not that no one could see them. The book was in Chesterton's hand.

Nietzsche was the first to speak. 'I don't want to be here,' he said, decisively. 'I'm still with Evangeline. I want to know what became of her and how it all worked out. I want to see if she ever met her brother. And what of that poor woman, Kate? I don't like women, it's true, but I know inside, she was brave. To ignore it!'

'For the greater good,' mused Chesterton, glancing at a billboard showing an illustrious actress. He didn't know it was Mathilde's great granddaughter.

'Of course, in your terms, the father was a hero,' he continued. 'A moral soldier forging his own path and to hell with society's norms. Mill was too, in his way, with his involvement with another man's wife. But I think Evangeline was all right.'

Both the men stared glumly at the pages of the book hoping to catch sight of the scene that had happened sometime in Evangeline's very long life. It was like waking from a favourite dream to which you can no longer return. In truth, they were both a little in love with the young Victorian girl who was now lost to sight and replaced by denim-clad shoppers. The book had nothing to show them.

Sighing in frustration, Chesterton got out his notebook and wrote "Evangeline Haverton (?)" under the heading "Others to Meet".

'I expect she married,' he said peremptorily, as Nietzsche peered over his shoulder. 'And we don't know her married name!' He snapped the notebook shut and looked around.

He found himself surrounded by mirrors which didn't lie. The fact that he was twenty-two stone usually didn't matter, but amidst all these young people he felt unusually large. But then he remembered that he couldn't be seen and for that was grateful, as it meant he could stop the unequal task of holding his stomach in. He let it go, allowing it to bulge cheerfully against his braces.

'They're mostly very thin,' he shouted over the heads of a group of sixteen year olds. 'It's extraordinary that they're all the same size!'

'Not so when you think about Athens,' replied Nietzsche,

finding some solace from losing Evangeline by remembering his books and his muses. 'Remember the Athenian ideal – this is just a modern expression.'

'Really!' retorted Chesterton. 'In body perhaps, but when you look into their faces you will see they are far from serene. If anything, it is a perversion of the old ways of beauty. Or at least it seems so to me. They make me think of my wife. That's the strange thing about monogamy. People think that to be monogamous you must stop wanting other woman. It's the opposite. Monogamy doesn't stop you wanting other men's wives, just that you want your own more!'

It was Nietzsche's turn to look doubtful.

'Now I know, my friend, that I had not much experience of women. Apart from the one who infected me with syphilis, and some say I did that on purpose in an effort to make myself mad – which worked!' he added as an afterthought. 'Yes, I know I'm not much experienced, but I doubt that you can ever love anyone so much that it excludes everyone else.'

'Like you said, you've not much experience of women.' For a moment Chesterton looked sad. He had loved his wife very much and had yet to find her in death. But possibly, one day, he would. It was only a matter of time, and for all he knew there was eternity to play with. That was why he didn't resent spending this time with the German. Even though he wouldn't have picked him, they were experiencing things together, and in a way finding shared ground.

'Shall we go on?' Nietzsche shouted over the head of a woman dressed head to toe in cashmere. Her baby, who could not have been more than a few weeks old, was wearing a designer label but the name meant nothing to either of the men who were standing the closest to him.

'Would you mind terribly if I had another go?' said Chesterton, rummaging in his knapsack for an offering of food. 'It's just that I've thought of something.'

'I don't think I should let you,' replied Nietzsche getting his hands on the book and bending it so hard, the spine squeaked. He was so used to combat that he did it as a matter of instinct. He rifled the pages irascibly.

'Now come on,' said Chesterton, cutting a slice of fruit cake on which he laid Wensleydale cheese and handing it to the German, over the head of the woman in cashmere who appeared not to have eaten for weeks. 'I'll explain my reasoning. Mr Mill was a consequentialist, was he not?'

Nietzsche nodded between mouthfuls of cake. 'Don't think you've got away with it. We haven't yet had a discussion about his kind of pleasure and the enormous vulgarity with which he wished to see it spread. Don't get me started on his dishonesty either! The man said he was after pleasure but it turns out he promoted something quite different. What's liberty and effort to do with pleasure, I ask you?'

'Well that's a big question. We could be here for hours. There are problems with consequentialism to be sure – how do you know that the thing you intend to happen, actually will?

'And how do you assess the different goods for the father – the mistress – the wife and the girl?' Nietzsche said glumly. 'And the baby!' he added, glancing into the pram. 'It leaves so much to chance – the happiness you think you are bringing about, may turn out to be a very different thing!'

Chesterton found himself agreeing. 'I mean, what a shock for poor Evangeline if she had ever found out the truth! And was he right to keep it a secret – the father I mean?' He paused. 'So, what if we compare – directly and at once –

Mill's type of outcome based morality with something quite different? A system that puts forward a logical basis to show that adultery is wrong!'

Nietzsche was absorbed in the crumbly Wensleydale, which had just then fallen into the baby's pram and which the infant was trying to eat.

'Do you see that? The human! He's trying to eat my cheese!' He stuffed the book in his pocket.

'Well never mind,' said Chesterton, his mind on his argument and attributing the remark to native German gluttony. 'I've still got plenty to spare.'

'*Nein*. No, It's not that...' began the German, but then he gave up. What did it matter if the baby could see them? Maybe the portal between birth and death was thinner than he had supposed. The journalist was driving at something.

'What I'm proposing, that I think is interesting, is that we compare directly a system that defines what is good by the *consequences* of an action with a system that ignores the outcome. A system where good is arrived at *regardless* of the outcome. Would that not make an interesting comparison, don't you think?'

Nietzsche had spent the last few minutes fishing about in the pram, trying to disengage the large piece of cheese from the baby's vice-like grip. He succeeded eventually, virtually taking it out of his mouth and the child let out a ferocious howl, screaming at the unkind ghost who had robbed him, at last, of his prize. The philosopher looked embarrassed.

'I didn't want him to choke!' he muttered.

'Well that was uncommonly kind!' roared Chesterton, as the baby screamed and the cashmere Mum fussed round. 'It was also an outcome based morality. You did something because of its outcome; not wanting little 'What's-It' to choke.'

'I did?'

'You did! Look – you're the philosopher. You must know Kantian ethics.'

'Of course I know the old idiot. A stiff and formal clyster pipe and the opposite to consequentialism. He thought he could define good without reference to what happens next.'

'That's right but what's a clyster pipe?' asked the journalist, getting up to leave. The baby's screams showed no sound of abating, and the mother had got out her phone.

'A tube used for injections. Usually in the bottom and bowels.'

'Oh, an enema! You're calling Herr Kant an enema! What an extraordinarily rude thing to say!' But he smiled a little as he said it, and the philosopher nearly smiled back.

'What page is Herr Kant?' Nietzsche asked to stop himself from doing so and tapping the book in his pocket. 'All right my fat English friend. All right, I will now let you win.'

* * * * * * * *

Konigsberg 1782

Immanuel Kant

The wind was getting up by the time the coachman turned the horses' heads. He knew it by the way the saplings bent towards the landau. From what he could see of the way the coachman held his hat, the servants knew it too.

'Where are we, madam?' he had already enquired on more than one occasion.

But the countess merely touched her wig and looked coquettish.

'Madam, I have already enquired, where is our location, precisely?' He leant forward and studied the road as the carriage spun along.

'It's just a little outing,' she replied soothingly, leaning over and daring to place a gloved hand on his breeches.

'Madam, please!' The small man drew himself up to his full height and gazed despondently forward.

'In a moment we will be able to see the splendour of the Pregl River from quite a different angle, and I propose we take some light refreshment beside her shores.'

Her companion looked horrified.

'Madam, what can you mean?'

'Some light refreshment. A little coffee maybe? I have heard there is an establishment near the water where one may stop and rest.'

Stuffed together in the carriage the two figures were odd companions. The man; waspish and nervy, shrinking away in a dusty great coat. The woman; smug and expansive, sheathed in an enormous silk gown. Countess Scheiffenberg relaxed. She had achieved her mission and would be able to report to her friends that the bachelor was even more surprising than they had supposed. Sallow skin, protruding rabbit eyes. But it was the size of his head that gave her the most delight. 'It is at least a foot in length. Front to back, no less,' her friend Baroness La Roche had asserted. 'And you, my dear, are charged to confirm it!'

Countess Scheiffenberg was now in a position of strength, being surely the only female in the land to have tempted Herr Kant to her carriage. His head was truly magnificent! A bold and bulging affair with a monumental forehead that bordered deliciously on the absurd. Maybe there was a close line between the lunatic and the genius. Maybe the man opposite sat there!

As she surveyed him from under her ostrich feather, she noticed that a vein lying just beneath his skin had begun to pulsate. She watched it swell and throb as the professor started to hum. 'And to our right,' she ventured, leaning forward, 'is the Hollenstein Castle which figured so prominently in the recent wars.'

The humming ceased abruptly as her companion turned towards her with as much agitation as if he had seen a highwayman.

'Repeat that, madam.'

'The Castle Hollenstein, my dear sir. It is much reputed.'

'Indeed.'

'It held out for several months against the siege of Konigsberg but,' she raised a gloved hand and simpered, 'I

107

am, without doubt, informing you of a fact with which you are well acquainted.'

The philosopher cleared his throat and looked at her as if she were a bug crawled out of a mattress.

'The Castle Hollenstein is in Teutgen. It follows therefore that we are also in Teutgen. But what, in Heaven's name, madam, would lead you to suspect that I might *wish* to be in Teutgen? I have no wish to be here, I have no wish to see this castle, and I have no wish to be with you! Instruct your man to turn this instant! The stress of such a journey is highly discomforting. I am too far from home and too much disrupted. Turn the carriage now!'

'My dear sir!'

'Immediately!'

Startled at being spoken to so in such a way, Countess Scheiffenberg tapped her cane on the floor and the carriage wheeled about to face the spring breeze coming straight from the east and Tartar territory. The philosopher drew the moth-eaten coat in closer and looked away. He didn't say another thing for the entire seven miles it took to trot the return to Konigsberg, past the Lutheran cathedral, past the civic building of the town hall, until the landau turned into the quiet street in which he lived. Konigsberg was the capital of East Prussia but its bustle was avoided in this secluded, tree-lined precinct which maintained its orderliness even on washdays, when everywhere else was flapping with sheets and linen.

As the landau drew to a stop, the liveried postilion jumped down and rushed round to lower the steps. Countess Scheiffenberg was not amused, and drawing a fan from inside her fox muff, fluttered it to display her displeasure.

'*Mein Professor!* I simply wished to bring a little

divertissement to the monotony of your life. I thought that a drive in the country could only be *agréable*.'

The philosopher said nothing but raised his hat in a gesture of politeness laced with rancour.

'I do not travel to foreign parts, madam. Seven miles is, on any man's reckoning, virtually a foreign state and, on the strength of that, I will wish you good day.'

Immanuel Kant strode into his hallway and handed his tricorn hat to the ancient servant who hovered by the stairs to the kitchen.

'Preposterous, Josef. Quite preposterous! How long is it since I left with that woman?'

'Two hours gone, sir. I was anxious for your return.'

'Quite so! I was anxious enough for it myself. Never again! The world of phenomena is an untrustworthy place, Josef. Mark it! What you experience as truth is not necessarily truth at all! Now, with the day so entirely disrupted, I will ask for a warm drink to be brought straight to the study, and we will dispense with the usual exercise. Enough! Quite enough!'

He handed his coat to the servant and walked briskly up the spiral staircase that separated the floors in the narrow town house. To say he ran would be an exaggeration, for Kant never ran. But his pace was quicker than normal and Josef felt his own blood ran faster at the excitement of it all. Having entered the household when he and his master were both young men, and being now both elderly men, he could honestly say that he couldn't remember a single time when the rhythm and motion of the day had been so interrupted. Not one! For thirty years the regime had been the same, as mechanical and ordered as the timepiece on the mantle. While the weeks of others were punctuated by days of rest,

109

Kant didn't go to church and hated distraction. So this day, when his master had not only been out of the house for several hours but spent them with a female, was as astonishing as a comet crossing the sky.

Josef boiled milk and took some roasted cocoa beans from the jar in which he kept them, crushing their shells before transferring them to the heated stone, where he pounded them again. He sweated slightly as he did it. His chest and arm always seemed to tighten when he exerted himself, but eventually the beans gave up their paste which he whisked into the liquid, adding sugar and spices before decanting some of the concoction into a bowl of his own. He tasted. The chocolate was good this month. The kitchen was Josef's domain and he prided himself that here, at least, there were new inventions and pleasures to be found. Little by little, he slipped them into their menu and waited for the response. Normally Kant would be so preoccupied reading, as he dined alone, that he would hardly notice what he was eating, and only remark later that he thought the 'peeled orange very fair.' Kant was a good master and their relationship was founded on complete trust. So Josef furnished his kitchen lavishly and prided himself on adding zest to this one small corner of their lives.

He had placed the china cup on the tray and had turned to mount the stairs when he heard a knock. It came from the door that led out to the street, the tradesman's entrance, but it was hardly a tradesman's knock. He tut-tutted and turned a deaf ear. Whoever it was, could wait. He didn't want his careful preparations ruined at the last.

'I have bought you warmed chocolate beans, sir,' he ventured, as he pushed open the green baize door. The master would normally be at his desk, writing or annotating, but today he was standing with his face turned towards a sulking fire which emitted more light than heat and not much of either. 'Chocolate beans, sir,' he repeated, 'straight from the Andes and bringing foreign climes to our door.'

The usually composed Immanuel swung round quickly. 'Do you mock me, Josef?'

'I beg pardon, Mannlich?'

'Do you mock me with talk of foreign climes? Surely you can see I am agitated enough by my experience.' Kant's head had the habit of nodding slightly when he was stirred, and his prominent eyes bulged like a rabbit.

'I do not, Master!' the grey-haired servant replied hotly. 'Indeed, I do not.'

Kant nodded and breathed self-consciously. He walked over to where Josef was rooted to the spot and touched him lightly on the arm, an intimacy which both would have found astounding were it not for the heightened emotion of the day.

'I am sorry for it then,' he said. 'But I will tell you, I thought that you were compounding the insult that has been done. For it quickly became apparent that the woman who drove me, did it not from genuine motives but because she wanted to entice an old fool into her carriage. She was using me, you see, Josef; exploiting me for some gain. A display to her friends, no doubt. And for a moment there, I thought the worse of you and thought you might be doing the same. But I misjudged you – and for that I am sorry.'

'Mannlich,' Josef used the old term which denoted a master of the university as well as one of the house, 'I would never use you in such a way.'

Kant found himself apologising all over again. 'No, no. You must forgive me, I was quite mistaken, but I will find it less easy to forgive the Countess. It is a great crime,' he continued, taking up the chocolate with a surprisingly clumsy hand, 'to use a man as a means to an end, whether that end be silliness or something more sinister. For a man is of value *above* all else only because he confers value *on* all else. Such is his humanity. Such is the ability that saves him from becoming an object or a beast. To become the means whereby another man profits, reduces him to something less than human.'

The servant inclined his head quietly, understanding far more than he let on. He knew, for example, that Kant was upset because his master lived so much in his head that the real world was a sort of canvas on which abstract ideas were drawn. So the abstraction became the experience, hollowed out and cold.

These drab November days were dark by late afternoon, so the old servant walked over to pull the curtains and make the room more cosy. The gloom was gathering and certainly there was a storm coming in from the Steppes. A raw Baltic wind announced it. He glanced down to the alley, for the study was at the back of the house and, seeing a movement in the shadows, remembered the unanswered door.

Kant had turned away and was rifling through some papers. 'Will that be all, master?'

'Yes. Indeed. I will see you at nine.'

Josef bowed his head and left, marvelling at the man's stamina for work which drove him as reliably as water in a mill race. But it was work without play and that was the tragedy – a tragedy for both of them.

The lamp in the corner of the kitchen threw dark shadows around the pots and pans hanging from the ceiling, and the blackened panes showed that night had fallen outside. Josef listened but could hear nothing, and reflected that the visitor had no doubt decided that his own fire was more urgent than any sale and gone off to find it. So he cupped his hands round the bowl, which had stood too long to be comforting, and stared into space. He had sat like it for some time, maybe half an hour, when the noise disturbed him again.

'Who's there?' Knees creaking, he rose to his feet but there was no answer, only the wind mewing against the window like an unhoused spirit.

He strained but there was nothing. No sign of life on this most desolate of nights, and not for the first time Josef wondered how it had come about that he should be sitting alone, in this high house, without having achieved in the span of all his years, any of the things that commonly counted. He had no money; no investments other than the leather pouch he kept in his closet that held the entirety of his wealth; no offspring or family to call his own. He had never been intimate with a woman, never felt that he belonged to someone, however briefly, and never known love. Served – yes, he had done that in plenty – but he was well aware that there was more. And here he was, gone grey, with a creaking frame, and time had covered over his hopes with mildewed years, so that now he would never know what it was that he had not found.

A particularly strong gust of wind knocked a branch against the window and Josef listened again. Surely that was something? A noise behind the storm? But he couldn't be certain, and drew his low chair closer to the hearth while he piled on logs. He had just sat down, and wrapped a blanket over his legs, when he heard the noise again. There was no mistaking it this time. Someone, or something, was at the door. 'Who's there?' he called again, making his way over and turning the key cautiously in the lock. His acquaintances in the market had warned him last Wednesday to beware of the intruders who were working the town.

He picked up the iron stopper, opened the door a few inches and peered outside. Nothing. He looked around; up and down the street, but there was no one there. Shaking his head and reflecting that it must have been a branch after all, he was about to close the door when something on the ground caught his eye. A sack. The noise must have been coal being delivered or an order he'd forgotten. But then the sack moved, and Josef saw that it was not a sack but a blanket, and that both it and the body it covered were lying in the dirt, with the wind whipping over it, and the snow starting to stick.

'Upon my soul!'

The old man bent down and pulled the cloth back. It was too dark to see much, but one glance told him all that he needed, and he had very little difficulty in scooping the bundle up, banging the door closed and stumbling to the fireside where he deposited his load.

For a moment he stood there gaping, but then he roused himself and turned away to snatch the kettle to the range and see what the larder would yield. Long years of solitude had dug deep into Josef and he had no fluency with words, so he busied himself with heating warm broth and fetching a quilt of feather. Until the silence in the kitchen became unnatural.

'What is your name?' he asked, thinking that it was actually the last thing he needed to know.

The figure merely shook its head and looked up at him with anxious eyes.

'Are you hungry then? You can tell me that, I warrant.'

'Yes.' The hair that hid the face was caked in dirt, but

Josef could see that it was straw coloured, grown light at the temples. The woman, if such she was, looked to be around forty years old, coarse and unkempt with blackened nails and a sodden shawl.

'Eat then.' He held up the bowl and some black bread which she grabbed at, dunking it in the broth and scooping it into her mouth before something could wrest it from her. The old man watched from a distance.

'Are you injured?'

She shook her head.

'Hunted then?' Again she shook her head between mouthfuls.

'What brings you here?' She looked away, her eyes roaming over the kitchen with the unashamed enquiry of the vagabond.

'You tell me nothing. I ask again, what is your name and what is your trouble?' She stared at him; as timid and wary as anything caught in a snare.

For the second time that hour, Josef approached, trying to close his nostrils to the smell. Her gown was putrid. She did not resist but allowed him to guide her, half dragging, to his room where he drew the blanket up, put the chamber pot within reach, and fetched a beaker of water which he placed on the stool, where he also kept his Bible.

The woman – the first female he had touched since he held his mother's hand – lay now, like a child on his bed. He was tempted to ease back the hair that stuck to her cheek but instead he left, turning the key in the lock. She would sleep now, but in the dark hours any amount of mischief could be done by a person of malice.

He found himself making the strange decision not to mention the woman when he took in the supper to Kant.

Normally they would have some little repartee; for his master took an interest in events below stairs, there being not many above. So Josef would tell him when the baker's boy brought gossip, or when a pig was killed, or a baby born to a neighbour they hardly knew. Hence, an event such as a woman slouched against the doorway was, strictly speaking, something he should have mentioned. But he didn't. And he didn't know why he didn't. Months later he would reflect, without dismay, how differently things could have been, had he mentioned her right at the start. This was his first deception and, in a curious way, also the last.

* * *

The fire was cold when he woke, stiff now from sleeping upright. He hadn't heard her in the night and there was no sound coming from his room. Noises from the street told him as accurately as any timepiece that he was running late.

He hurried to smarten up, put eggs on to boil and prepare the coffee. Then he shoved everything on a tray in unaccustomed disorder and made it into the dining room just as his master opened the door. Normally Josef would have been in there some fifteen minutes earlier, folding back the shutters, preparing the table, standing stiffly to attention as the philosopher wound his way down for his breakfast. But today none of this was done, and Josef had to clump down the tray with the coffee splashing everywhere, before hurrying over to let the light flood into the room.

He needn't have worried for his master appeared not to have noticed.

'I am at the university today, Josef. See to it that the papers for the third lecture, first semester are prepared.'

He nodded. 'Sir.'

'It is only the most elementary lecture,' K
dryly. 'Nevertheless, it will probably tax them.'

'The Categorical Imperative, master?' said Josef
keep his eyes ahead of him and not glance anxiously at the
door.

'Quite so. Now tell me Josef, did you sleep?'

'Sir?' It was an unheard of enquiry.

'Did you sleep? Because I did not. I arose several times
and went to the window. There was a fearsome storm and
now there is snow. But, at a point in the night, the sky was
clear; very clear indeed. Lots of stars about. And I said to
myself, "Two things fill my mind with ever new and
increasing admiration – the starry Heavens above me and the
moral law within me." It's a good little aphorism, don't you
think?'

'Very good, sir.'

'And what do you think it means, sir?' Kant was not
mocking him. When the conversation touched on the
philosophic, his servant became a companion.

'It means that you are as certain of the inner moral
impulse as you are of the stars above, and in awe of both,
sir. That's what I think it must mean.'

'Josef, you are a marvel,' said Kant, pushing away the
breakfast plate and mopping his lips with the napkin.
'Though, I have to say, in all our years together I have never
yet been served with an underdone egg! Two in fact!
Nevertheless, I can forgive you anything when you interpret
my thoughts as precisely as I hatch them. We are due at the
place till twelve.'

There was no need for Kant to say this, for when he gave
his lectures he left the house and returned within seconds of

117

ccuracy. Nevertheless, it formed part of the regular morning exchange, though it was peculiarly unwelcome to his servant on this particular day because Josef had completely forgotten about it.

'Very good, sir.'

He clattered down to the kitchen, ran up the stairs to stuff the papers into their leather satchel, tidied up the morning room, ran down to the kitchen again, hesitated outside his chamber door, built up the fire, carried in the coal, paused again beside his chamber, brushed down Kant's overcoat and swept the floor. Then, finally, with just minutes to go, he summoned all his resolve and unlocked the door.

The room was dark and stuffy. He crept as close to the bed as he dared. The chamber pot had been used and Josef covered it with a towel before emptying the slops out of the window. He found himself fascinated by the contents. It seemed an unnatural intimacy to know this about her when he didn't yet know her name. She stirred in her sleep and Josef backed away. Then, as an afterthought, he placed a platter of bread on the floorboards.

Kant gave him a quizzical look as he panted up the stairs with the overcoat. 'Are you out of sorts, Josef? Things seem a little tardy. Is something awry with you today?'

'No, no, master, all in order. I beg pardon. Thank you.'

'You have my papers?'

Josef took up the satchel, silently hoping that he had picked up the right sheaf in his distraction, and patted it conspiratorially. Kant gave him another queer look, raising his eyebrow. 'Quite,' he said as if in thought. 'Quite.'

'Yes indeed. Quite so, sir,' Josef muttered, shepherding

him out of the door and turning up the street. He glanced at the basement window as they passed by and couldn't be absolutely certain that he didn't see movement within.

* * *

The lecture hall had something of the bear-baiting pit. Built in the round, the lecturer stood on a podium while his students lolled and chatted just feet away, resting their writing papers and sometimes their heads on the stuffed leather banister that separated tutor from mob. Kant was so short he had to stand on a box to allow the furthest rows to see him.

At precisely ten minutes past nine, Immanuel Kant took up position and motioned for the exit to be closed. No one would come in, or out, for the next three hours. The students took their feet off the benches and did their best to settle down. All but the very keen, who sat in the front row, looked as if they were readying themselves for something unpleasant. Kant cleared his throat and regarded his audience with disdain. If it had been possible to have looked down on them, he would.

'The title of today's lecture is "The Moral Law Within",' he began, glancing at the notes which he knew by heart, but pleased with the new opening.

Some of the older students who were sitting the year again groaned; their younger contemporaries looking round in embarrassment.

'Gracious God! Not again!' shouted a heckler. 'We've heard it before, Herr Kant.'

'God has nothing whatsoever to do with it!'

These undergraduate lectures were routinely humiliating. However, as Professor, it was a contractual obligation to face the lower orders for eight weeks of the year, and these lectures paid enough to allow him to work on *The Groundwork* which he knew was seminal. 'If you had listened to anything, Meister Claus, you would know that my starting point is logic not God. As the language of religion is that of assertion, we would be well advised to leave God quite to one side.'

The students fidgeted and Kant shuffled his papers.

'The Moral Law Within. A man is compelled to act in response to its call, but only by doing so does he become moral. For there are many reasons, gentlemen, why a man might appear to do a good act, and yet few of them are what they seem. Let us rehearse those reasons.

'Suppose a shopkeeper reduces his prices so that his customers pay reduced cost. That shopkeeper might be praised. He might, indeed, be called a "good shopkeeper", but could he be called a good man? I see you nodding, Meister Glaundel, but you are mistaken.

'Well, he'd be a good man in my book,' called the unruly second year who had spent more time in various shops of a dubious nature than he had in studying, 'Especially if the shop was a tavern!' The audience roared in appreciation.

Kant shook his head above the din. 'He would not be a good man and it would not be a good act, for he would merely be following a command of the lower order – a hypothetical rather than a categorical imperative.'

He glanced over at Josef who was deaf to it all and staring straight ahead. Sometimes, he wondered whether his servant was indeed the only man there who had the faintest idea what he was trying to say.

* * *

They had been a long three hours with the audience particularly boorish. So both men hurried through the wintery slush with unusual haste. For Kant it was the call of chapter twenty-nine of *The Groundwork*. For Josef it was something else.

He didn't know what it was he expected, but No 32 Kleinvarst Street was intact. No broken windows, no ruffians helping themselves to his ham, no women rifling through the papers in his master's study. He served lunch with as much haste as was decent, and made sure the portions were small so Kant would not linger. He need not have worried. The philosopher, far from being discomforted by the heckling of the morning, seemed to be in an unusually good temper. 'Chapter twenty-nine awaits,' he said, leaving most of his food untouched, 'and it will start with an exposition of the noumenal as opposed to the phenomenal!'

The woman was quite different from the creature Josef had imagined. A few hours' sleep and a pitcher of water had removed much of the dirt. She was younger than he had thought. No more than thirty now.

'Forgive me my delay,' he said.

'I was broken and couldn't find my feet.'

The woman spoke in the artisan dialect of the town. 'Let me do that,' she offered as he riddled the fire.

'No indeed. You are in distress and I can help, and that is quite enough.'

She stared at him with an awkward, sideways slant of the head and he knew she needed some task.

'Very well then. You may cut the meat and butter the bread, and fetch the apple from the hatch, and then you may tell me your story.'

Her movement on the flagstones had something of the wraith about it; fleeting and transient as if the motion she made was too ephemeral to carry her for long. But her feet were clad in soft leather; the only thing of quality she wore.

They sat and ate together, with the woman serving him as if she were his servant.

He learned that she had come from the Strechenhaussen, where the leather workers lived on the far side of town.

'Well now,' he said finally, after he had watched her eat like one possessed. His statement hung in the air.

'My name is Ada,' she repeated, apparently searching for an entry. They were both aware of the moment. It was as if she was searching for the underbelly of the thing, where the entrance would be flabby and soft.

'I have one child,' she said finally, laying down her fork.

'I had a husband and four – no more than a month gone. But first the babe, then my girls were struck by the pox. I buried all three within a week, three bodies in the common grave and my husband who joined 'em in days.' The woman looked at him, stating the facts calmly although the voice kept catching in her throat. It was the same voice that would have sung to her children, thought Josef.

'You have no one to support you? No family?'

'No sir.'

Josef liked talking to her and the warmth coming off this surprising creature. He liked, too, the way she addressed him. Respectful. And the hands, which were worn yet quiet, the grey slate of her eyes and the unaccountable calmness. He liked having her in his kitchen.

'I do have a son, sir. My one remaining child. And as precious to me as….' she paused, not able to find the treasure to match him.

'Hans, he is called. Hans, sir.'

He nodded, inviting her to go on.

'Hans ...' her voice trailed off. 'He had loved them all, you see, sir. And then his playmates were gone. And he felt... a new care. Responsibility for me. For his mother! And he – only a child himself. He didn't know right from wrong.'

Josef wondered what was coming but found that – whatever it was – he would view it from a neutral ground. He knew he could not condemn her.

'He broke into a rich man's house and stole. Sufficient to fill my purse with coin. But he is not a thief by nature – knows no art nor guile and many people had seen him. So – within the hour – the burgers had come. And now my boy will hang.'

She said it starkly, with space around the words, so that it seemed the lad was already there; hanging in the kitchen, suspended from his mother's thin lines. But there was no resignation in her eyes. Nor sorrow really. Instead they shone with some ardour that Josef could not quite account for. He spread his hands and looked to the floor, not knowing what on earth he should say.

'Is he condemned already?' he said.

'He is not!' He looked up at her, catching some note. She hurried on, as if the words must come out in a rush.

'The man who will try him can be bought. It is known that he is corrupt. We have at least been lucky in that – the judge is known for corruption. I know I can save my son.'

The kitchen itself evaporated. There was only this – the woman wrapped in the shawl, sitting in the chair and the flagstones cold at her feet. Josef could have drawn it with a stencil; so sharply outlined it was.

'How much would it take to achieve such a thing?' he heard himself ask.

She shook her head dismissively. 'Five hundred gulden. Maybe less…. but that would be safe.'

Five hundred gulden, give or take a few cents, was almost exactly the amount that Josef had in his closet. Collected over a lifetime of work. His only possession and the only thing he had in the world.

* * *

When Kant had been a young man, he had been affected by headaches so crippling he could no longer work. The Konigsburg quacks applied every remedy, all of which were useless, so Kant fell back on himself. He found that if he walked rapidly, breathing through his nostrils, the pain eventually subsided, though four miles were needed to be sure. So every day he walked; up and down the avenue, with his servant trotting along beside, armed with an umbrella to shield his master from various extremes of weather. The citizens of the avenue set their clocks by this rite.

Despite his inner turmoil, Josef was not late for the walk. He was never late for his duties.

'All is not what it seems,' his master began as he launched himself onto the street, motioning for Josef to walk beside him. 'That is why we must prefer the noumenal to the phenomenal world, and I will tell you why!' Josef had to adjust his thoughts, slow down his emotions and spice up his intellect to keep pace with his master, who was twirling his stick in excitement as he set off at rapid pace. 'Look around you, Josef, and you see the world of phenomena. Everything – this stick, those trees, all that we can touch, all we experience, all atomic material – is phenomena. Even those around us,' he paused. 'But the world of phenomena is dangerous. Illusory and not safe. How do I know that this stick is a stick, or that it is precisely three of the clock? I don't …and can never… know that!'

Kant's bulbous eyes gleamed with mischief, suspecting his servant to be way out of his depth.

'But I do know, master,' Joseph replied at length. 'I do know because I must *believe* my watch when it tells me that it is three of the clock. I must believe it in order to function.'

Kant stopped so that his companion almost bumped against him. 'Ah! But that's exactly the point,' he said in jubilation. 'It's just a belief – and a false one at that! There's no such thing as "o'clock"? What is it? A construct fashioned by man which he can harness and put to use. You obey it because it's demanded. But you obey a shadow. I'm not saying you're wrong to obey it – we all do. But one can't trust this shadowy world because what you *think* you experience may not be what actually *is*. In the dark, something coiled could be a viper or it could be a rope. There is no way of knowing. It is not a solid truth. Only the noumenal world, the thing in itself, *das Ding an Sich*, is true.'

Josef was still so infused with his interior dilemma that his master's words – normally so inaccessible, suddenly sprang to life.

'If our senses deceive us, they are not useful in a moral dilemma?' he said carefully.

Kant swung round.

'Yes. Exactly this is so! Useless as a ground. What is needed is a thing that is never deceived, that neither bends with the will, nor flinches with emotion. Something that has more of the noumenal realm about it than any world of the senses. What is it that is incorruptible, Josef? That cannot be something it's not?'

He shook his head, anxious not to be distracted from the subject on which he'd embarked.

'If you mean a virtue, sir, then I would say that courage cannot be corrupted. It allows you to take some action when all around seems bleak.' He thought of the look in her eye at the prospect of saving her son.

'Ahha!' said Kant in triumph 'Wrong! Courage can be misapplied and used for a bad end. A courageous thief is just better!'

Josef winced – he hadn't thought of that. It would be brave, indeed, to bribe the judge!

'Affection sir! Affection and regard. Both of those seem good in themselves.'

'Bah!' spat Kant as if he had tasted something rotten. 'You can't base morality on those two imposters! No, no, Josef. The only thing that is incorruptible is a good will itself! Consider! The moment the good will ceases to wish for good, it destroys itself and dissolves. A good will can never be anything less than itself. A good will can never be bad.'

Kant shot Josef a sideways look. But the dutiful servant merely kept pace and stared straight ahead. They had been up and down the avenue twice and were turning again at the top. His boots were leaking and feet beginning to freeze. But he couldn't let that affect him. He was considering what his master was saying.

'If a person were to give away all his wealth, sir, and it arose from a good will – would that be the right thing to do?'

'That depends!' replied Kant impatiently.

Josef was silent. His master shot him a look from under his eyebrows.

'What do you mean, man? Explain!'

Josef kept his head down. 'If a person was approached by another and the first knew that they needed help. And it would take all his money to help them. Should he give them that help?' It was a simple question and he wanted a simple reply.

'Probably not! It sounds like a poor sort of plan! He would be doing it for emotion to start with!'

'Yes' said Josef thoughtfully.

'And that is what I was saying – to the student oafs. A hypothetical imperative – done for some kind of end – is never a moral choice. It only flatters the self.'

'Yes sir. Done to make one feel good.'

Kant snorted. 'It would not make one feel good! To give away all of one's money!'

Josef strode on, so that now Kant had to keep pace.

'There is more to a life than one's money, Master,' he was astounded by his newly found voice. But Kant hardly seemed to hear him, continuing as he was with his own train of thought.

'The question centres on logic. Is the action one that would – in all circumstances – be good? If someone were to give away all his money! Bah! What would that do to the world?'

'I think he might not starve. Let us assume – for the argument Master – that his position was such that he would not starve.' Kant nodded gravely, assessing this addition. He tilted his head, considering.

'Then – maybe. It would arise from a good will, and it might be universalisable. If there were sufficient funds to support him so that he did not need this wealth.' He tipped his head again.

'Does what the money is used for – where it is destined

– come into consideration?' asked Josef who was starting to sweat; though whether it was from the heightened exertion, or because the terrifying choice was becoming nearer, he couldn't quite be sure.

'That depends!' Kant said, curtly.

'The consequences don't matter?'

'That's not what you asked! The act in total takes all into account. Not the outcome but what the act is. So…. if it arises from a good will; is such that anyone in the same situation should also do the same thing; is done not for reward and treats no man as a means to an end. Then…. this seems to me to be moral.' Kant's eyes bulged with impatience.

'Done to save a life?'

'Save a life, condemn a life – what matters? It is the act itself we are considering, not what the action can do.'

'If the money were to be used for an evil act in order to support a lenient one?' asked Josef getting as close to the matter as he dared and hoping that he would not alert his master. But Kant was so far gone into the logic of the problem that he couldn't hear the tightness in his servant's voice. He tossed his head dismissively.

'Well then of course not!' he said in astonishment. 'That is part of the act. To do something dishonest would not be universally wise. Dishonesty would flourish – there would be no such thing as honesty, if dishonesty were always allowed. Of course this is not right! It is immediately obvious this thing!'

'But if the dishonest act would save an honest life?' Josef's voice rose with the heightened emotion. 'Would it not be a good man who did it?'

For the second time that day, Kant's walk came to a halt. He faced his servant squarely; two old men with their coats buttoned against the cold, their breath coming fast from exertion.

'I do not understand Josef, why this worries you so. Such philosophical questions should be left to the learned. It is not your worry this thing – it is not your...' he paused, trying to introduce a delicacy into his sentence but failing to find it. 'It is not your place, this concern.'

For the briefest of seconds, Josef met him in the eye, before looking swiftly away.

'No Meinlich, forgive me. My impertinence!'

Kant snorted and wheeled about. 'Enough of this idle chatter.' He nodded grimly to himself as the full extent of it came home, 'And another disruption to habit. This is not good Josef – all this talk. We have only done five or six lengths!'

'Indeed sir!' the servant replied, appearing thoroughly crestfallen.

'But – now I have no appetite. Come! We will go home!'

As Josef held the umbrella, keeping a respectful distance, he let Kant's words sink in. It would take a few days more to come to a decision – but he had heard little enough to dissuade him.

* * *

'Teleology. Telos. Tel-e-ology'. He played around with the unfamiliar word, rolling it around his mouth like a boiled sweet. It tasted like it sounded – liquid and unconstrained. Open-ended, fluid, undecided. He knew from Kant's crabbed notebook-hand that teleological thoughts spelt danger, being, as they were, the opposite of the dutiful, deontological life he had lived until now. Telos, translating as "purpose", and subdividing into myriad lanes and byways seemed to him spectacularly unresolved. Any good might come from it – or, indeed, any bad.

Kant was at his writing desk holding his head, for he felt one of his headaches coming on. It never crossed his mind to walk a few minutes early. He looked up in surprise when his servant entered.

'I didn't call you, Josef. Is it time?'

'It is your shoes, Master,' he said holding up a pair of Kant's dress shoes that he rarely, if ever, used.

'What of them?'

'They are worn! I will have them repaired, sir.'

Kant eyed him as if the man had two heads. 'Yes' he said, curtly. 'You come in to tell me this?'

Josef nodded, moving his weight from leg to leg and wishing he could find the words that would rescue them both.

'I..... I need to go to the far side of town!'

Kant nodded swiftly, taking up his pen. 'Yes. You will be back for my meal?'

Josef cleared his throat, wishing he could just ask him. Wishing he could say, "Master I am in very grave danger of giving away all my money and I would that you could find the words to prevent me. Because I know it is foolish, but I have developed an attachment and I find that the thought of her – and what this might do – drives me out of my reason," but not a single one of those words came out. Instead he said 'Of course Sir, I will not be long. I will go when the weather is fair,' bowed his head slightly and backed out of the room.

For the next five or six days he experienced acute distress. He would go to the closet, bring out the pouch and look at the coins, even counting them one evening. They were so valuable to him. The pouch stood for all of his days – all the injustice and the smallest of wrongs that can exist between master and servant, even when they are both well disposed. The money tipped the scales back in his direction; it was his recompense for a life. But Ada! At the thought of her, his mind grew weak. This money could save her; it might even... He closed his eyes and allowed his thoughts free rein. It might even buy her, if such was not too gross a suggestion. It would make her grateful to him! And if it didn't! Well – no matter. He would have helped her and that was enough. His bad act was not so serious. The magistrate had already done wrong. He was not corrupting an innocent. His money would be put to good use.

The days grew colder and then very cold. The keenest frost that most people could remember. The philosopher and his servant huddled themselves in their blankets and kept the fires stoked. Even so, the hoar still collected on the inside of the panes.

Josef continued in confusion, thinking of her every day. He did not wash his pillow for fear of washing her off. At night, when he used the chamber pot, he thought of her and the dark surplus matter her body had expelled. He vowed he would plant a seed in the soil beneath the window.

It was the shortest day of the year, a few days before Christmas – a feast they never kept – when Josef made up his mind. He waited till after Kant's constitutional, then took the satchel he had already prepared with his master's dress shoes inside. His destination was on the far side of town, reached through unfamiliar streets. He glanced at the ruffians from under his eyebrows and clasped the satchel more closely.

The smell of the tannin announced he was there; vats of boiling water with hides hung out to dry. He stooped into one or two hovels. 'Can you repair these shoes? Do you know a master craftsman? Might you point out his dwelling?' but he couldn't bring himself to ask the one question he wanted to ask, until an urchin approached him, his eyes registering surprise to see such a gentleman in his neighbourhood.

'Have you a penny, mister, a penny for me guts?'

Josef held up a coin, letting it gleam in the sun and then finally mouthing, 'You may have it if you lead me to the woman called Ada,' and within a few moments he was standing up to his ankles in muck and gazing at a door that was closed tight, with a shutter hanging from a broken pane, and he was both minus the coin and richer than he'd been all the time that he'd held it.

'Who's there?' he heard from within. It was her voice he was sure. And then she was there, standing before him, smoothing down her apron and mumbling something. Josef reached into his satchel and presented his master's worn shoes. Then he took out the pouch of his savings and handed them over, gazing all the time at her face. And what he saw surpassed all his expectations. Her delight brought quite as much joy as the coins had ever promised. Everything was to be played for. He bent his head and went in.

* * * * * * * *

From somewhere Nietzsche had found a postscript. It was a crisp piece of paper, not mildewed or old, but sharp and fresh from the copier. He read it aloud as Chesterton took the pince-nez off his nose and rubbed his eyes which were tired with the effort of seeing.

'It's a postscript,' said Nietzsche in his thick German accent. 'I will read it, just as it's written…

`Josef Steigler gave Ada the money which signified all his life's savings. The boy was tried a few weeks later and was dismissed of all charges of theft – a verdict for which few could account. Ada developed a friendship with Josef, an outcome with which he was delighted and for several months she visited him. Later in the same year, Kant's house was rifled and a number of valuables taken. On investigation, it was found that Josef had allowed the woman to remain inside while he and his master were out. The servant was arraigned for complicity, although he always denied it, and was forced to leave Kant's employ. He died within a few months whilst serving a prison sentence; penniless and alone. Neither the woman nor his master visited him, nor were able to assist.

'Immanuel Kant was important in his own lifetime, and is regarded as pivotal in every respect; his work providing a rational basis for human rights. His principles of universalisation and the refusal to treat another as a means to an end, continue to be relevant long after his lifetime.'

Nietzsche folded the paper carefully and put it in the

inside pocket of the coarse woollen jacket he had all the time been wearing. It settled next to the book.

'Pfff!' he sniffed derisively, 'I said he was a stiff and formal clyster pipe, did I not? What a thing to do to that poor man called Josef. I quite varmed to Josef. He forged his own vay and all that.'

Chesterton finished rubbing his eyes, replaced his glasses and blew his nose with an enormous blue and white handkerchief. It was the one he had used as a plate when they had first met on the slope of the mountain, and it still had the residual smell of mustard.

'He must be right, of course,' he reflected, addressing the philosopher directly. 'Kant, I mean. He must be right.'

'*Vhy* do you say that?' Having been so long in the company of German speakers, Nietzsche was finding it hard to relinquish. He allowed a heaviness to creep into his accent, to stress his illustrious roots.

'Please speak normally. You're too annoying!' Chesterton glared at him, and Nietzsche crumbled. Of late he had less will for a fight.

'But I, too, am German!'

'Do you think I don't know that? Besides, there was no Germany in Kant's time. He lived in East Prussia and Konigsberg is now in Russia, as you very well know. But I am interested, Herr Professor, what did you make of that? Don't you agree that Kant in some sense is right, even though his theory is harsh?'

'*Nein,* Kant is not right,' said the professor emphatically, lacing his fingers together and cracking the bones. 'You see, my journalist companion, the mistake of all these philosophers is to base everything on an assumption that is, and always is, false. Take Kant's "noumenal world" that he spoke of. His theory rests solely on that! Like Plato's eternal forms, he puts forward some other world as being true, which in Kant's eyes is the realm of pure Reason. Yet, this noumenal world is a thing without properties. It cannot have a relationship with anything with properties, or anything that exists for that matter, and still Kant's system rests on its head. And when we come to examine this shadowy place? Of course, hah! We can't find it! Still less can we refute it. There is nothing I could say to Herr Kant that would force him to adjust his noumenal world, still less agree that it's a thing of fiction and hence has no moral standing. It's like that with all metaphysical notions – your precious Aquinas was the same! At least Kant keeps God in the distance. But Reason or God, they are both just as empty. Neither can be refuted and yet such dictats they issue! Such commands we are forced to obey!'

Chesterton listened intently. This was the first time he had heard the philosopher speak philosophically. He remembered that the man was brilliant, despite his predilection for violence and several unfortunate habits.

'Nevertheless,' he parried. 'If there is no such thing as "justice" then think what wrongs we would have to endure. The poor man would lose to the man with more money; that slave girl we saw, would know with less clarity why abuse is always so wrong. The whole notion of abuse is destroyed by Kant, and respect for each other introduced in its place. Justice is necessary and Right – and I use that word with a deliberate capital. The world must have a stab at justice, and so the notion of Justice must in some sense exist. Surely that's all that Kant meant? He didn't mean there was a place you could find it.'

'Obviously not!' It was the professor's turn to glare. 'Do you think I'm so stupid? What I'm saying is that there is not even a *theoretical* place where it could exist, and so therefore it can't be promoted.'

'What do all these philosophers have in common?' he continued. 'A distinct distaste for "what is". They have a notion of how the world works but want to change it, to make it better. My brilliance was to uncover this error and demonstrate that there's no reason even to try. Justice or empathy doesn't make the world better because it is dishonest to the true individual – the man who wants all for himself. He alone is supreme.'

'Oh, we're back on that old pancake are we?' observed Chesterton wearily. 'You're saying that there is no connection between what something *is* and what something *ought to be*. That they are different types of statement. I've heard that one somewhere before. Who's that you're poking around with – be careful man, it's a delicate book. The philosopher Ayer? I knew him! He was around when I was alive. My word, we are getting modern. There are others I want to see more!'

'The book shows that Ayer is most fun,' Nietzsche was attempting to be conciliatory. 'His story is a Detective tale. Right up your street, my fat one! Didn't you invent a sleuth by the name of Father Brown? Besides, you've just had two philosophers of your choosing. It's time I had my choice.'

'Very well,' said Chesterton. 'What date do we start?'

The philosopher studied the pages. 'The nineteen sixties,' he said. 'Cambridge in the sixties, though why there, I don't know. I thought Ayer had come from Oxford.'

'He did,' said Chesterton lightly. 'A generation or two after me. I met him when he was a lad. It will be interesting to see what became of him.' And with that, he lit another pipe and settled himself back on a boulder. Nietzsche let the book fall open and they both peered into its pages.

* * * * * * * *

CAMBRIDGE 1969

A J Ayer

Cambridge in the sixties was a heady, hedonistic place, and no one was more wildly self-indulgent than the Director of Studies who taught French. Brilliant, dishevelled, mostly drunk, a smoker of cheap cigarettes and instigator of parties so wild that the elder dons shunned him at breakfast, Francis Delroy classed Sartre among his friends and Sam Beckett among his admirers. Increasingly homosexual, he nevertheless appreciated females, especially the pretty French waitresses who took summer jobs in college.

He wasn't obviously attractive to look at, being too short and unkempt to be anywhere near handsome. But he had terrific charisma. He reeked of sex and, as his lovers emerged more open-minded than previously, he was never short of good friends. Plenty came back for more. Delroy would be at a party, surrounded by students, and something would pass – an energy, an arched eyebrow – and within minutes they would have disappeared whilst everyone else tried to fill the gap. No one ever quite could.

Even so, Delroy also had detractors. His preference for smoking joints whilst teaching students annoyed his more upstanding colleagues who complained about the smell. These same people also muttered at his habit of arriving staggeringly drunk for nine o'clock lectures, and having whisky on the podium as he spoke. They felt it unseemly, as indeed it was. He annoyed the Dean, whose liberal Christianity was pushed to the limits. He annoyed the intellectuals of both the far left and right by being deeply offensive to both. He annoyed the porters who would regularly have to remove an undesirable "friend" from the college precincts but, more than anyone, Delroy annoyed his wife.

Cathy Delroy was a sort of stellar opposite to her husband. Petite and orderly, she dressed in twin set and pearls and wore her hair in formidable beehives. She divided her time between the Mother's Union, of which she was President, being the only one in the group to be childless and hence have the time, and the Cambridge branch of the Christian Order for Compassion and Knowledge. She had been a virgin at the time of her marriage, and did her best to keep herself as close as possible to that state of grace ever after. She disliked Delroy's sudden urgency, the stabbing certainty of his moves, and the distasteful mess of ecstasy. She disliked sex and disliked her husband for wanting it, and disliked him even more for having it – with everyone other than herself. She threw herself with vigour into her work; a tireless, bustling woman who wore down the mothers with her exhortations to swap breast for bottle and even got on the nerves of the less compassionate of the compassionate Christians. She was just so sure.

Nicholas Giles, son of the Tory MP, whose family seat in Huntington was reluctantly opened to the public to pay the death duties when the old earl died, was Delroy's friend and lover. Lord Giles the younger was as debonair as Delroy was scruffy. "A sort of Kantian antinomy" was how he described their friendship. Dazzlingly brilliant, he was the natural heir to the Logical Positivist movement of forty years ago and regularly dined with Ayer who, elderly now, was still a force to be reckoned with when he visited them from Oxford. Giles appeared as unconcerned about Delroy's liaisons as he was about paying his taxes. They were just a sort of natural calamity that followed anything good. 'Met anyone interesting today?' he would ask, leaning back in his chair and drawing on an expensive cigar.

The May Ball was early in 1969, being the second rather than the third week in June. By great good fortune the committee had secured Johnny Cash and it was rumoured that Gainsbourg and Birkin might even turn up. With the wealth of centuries behind it, the May Ball Committee decided that this would be something to remember. So they decked the Cam with floodlights, lit the avenue with lanterns and dressed Old Court in black satin. Only the tree in the centre was left naked, save for a hundred candles tied to her lower limbs. Dodgem cars were hired and a rickety helter-skelter attached to the chapel wall. Ponies and traps ferried the guests up and down the avenue, drinking Bollinger and laughing insouciantly with the habitual bray of the privileged. The scene was set for calamity.

Cathy Delroy was the first to arrive at the pre-ball dinner; alone and overdressed, in an outdated mink stole and fuchsia dress that bulged in all the wrong places. The Master's Lodge had been made over to senior members of college, so anyone who hadn't fled to London sought refuge there. Ayer, up from Oxford, took his place near the Master with Giles seated next to him. The Dean and his wife were on opposite sides of them. Various dons were dotted about. Cathy Delroy had placed herself near a visiting lecturer from Ohio. Delroy staggered in late. Giles hardly glanced at him, while Cathy took a charitable interest in the Master's most recent ulcer.

'*Benedictus Benedicatur, Amen.*' Grace was perfunctory as the meal was really only a supper – a welcome retreat before the rout of the night.

'Is Bertie coming?' said the Master, brushing off Cathy's concern as dismissively as he shook out his table napkin. He addressed his remark to Giles.

'Shouldn't think so,' replied the latter, pouring him some Chardonay. 'Better things to do I'd imagine. Isn't he in London for the week, Freddie?'

'I believe so, though I cannot prove it.' Everyone laughed, apart from Cathy who didn't understand the joke. 'And that was our first great tragedy,' continued Ayer, smiling urbanely at his companions. 'That the verification principle was itself quite incapable of being proved.'

'Though you shot yourselves in the foot, your ideas were first rate.' The Master was a scientist and looked fondly on the legacy of the positivists. 'But it's hard to disagree with a movement that puts science, at its centre. Long time ago now though, Freddie, long time ago.'

'Indeed, and most of it wrong. Though I do think that we were on the right lines.'

'You were and you still are,' said Giles with just the faintest whiff of the disciple about him. 'And it remains my intention to demonstrate it.'

Alfred Jules Ayer groped around in his pocket, found the gilt cigarette case he was looking for and placed it on the table in readiness. He had a sort of well-bred lizard look about him, with lidded eyes that cloaked with charm the fierce intellectual reserves. Women found him irresistible and he them, and the visiting lecturer from Ohio had to be quite rude in ignoring her immediate companions to lean over and get his attention.

'Professor Ayer,' she began.

'My dear.'

'I was wondering whether you might explain your theory to me?'

'And why would I do that, my dear?'

She looked taken back. 'History will say it was an important theory. Why would I pass on the chance to get it from source? Besides I don't like to lag behind.'

'The Professor's theory,' Cathy was acidic, 'has never made any real sense.'

'Well that's entirely how it should be,' he smiled again with hardened eyes. Women had their own preserve and they should stay there. They were delightful on the dance floor, delightful in the bedroom but irritating when attempting logic.

'Oh, Professor,' continued the woman from Ohio. 'Just give me the abstract idea.' She knew it, of course. She was as well versed as anyone in the thing dubbed 'Emotivism', but she wanted to hear it from him.

'What's your discipline, my dear?' Ayer leaned forward so he could see her down the table, glancing playfully at Giles as he did so. 'Your field, so to speak.'

'I'm concerned with why things are wrong,' she said, leaning back in her chair and narrowing her eyes – careful not to give too much away. 'That's my personal interest. Professionally I'm a teacher of communication – an exciting field to be in.'

The table looked as if it could withhold its excitement. Delroy burped quietly to himself and reached clumsily for the decanter.

'Where the hell are all the waiters tonight anyway?' he said to no one in particular.

Ayer took her on. 'If you must know,' he said, witheringly,

'My theory of Emotivism suggested that all communication – your word – is just that. Mere babble, without truth or certainty, unless it falls into one of the two camps of meaning that do, actually, exist.'

'The two camps being the analytic and the synthetic,' added Giles, looking bored.

'The analytic is certainly true. So let's see. What's an unmarried male called, my dear, or don't you ever meet them in Ohio?'

'Available?' she replied, with a pearly laugh.

The table roared. Even Cathy joined in. Ayer was laughing too.

'Available, maybe! But that's not quite a definition, is it? I mean you could get an unmarried male who rather prefers it that way – not available – quite the opposite in fact. No, commonly in this country we would call an unmarried male a "bachelor."'

The American pouted. But inside she was pleased. Good – they were accepting the rouse.

'Oh, so you want a definition?' she said. 'Well, of course an unmarried male's a bachelor. Goes without saying doesn't it?'

'Precisely.' Ayer tapped the cigarette case with a well-manicured hand. 'So an analytic statement says something that is necessarily true; cannot be refuted. A tautology if you like.'

'Says the same thing twice,' explained Delroy helpfully.

'Almost mathematical; like $1 + 1 = 2$,' added Cathy.

'Yeah?' The lecturer fiddled with the bread by the side of her plate. 'So?'

'That's one camp,' said the Dean who hadn't spoken till now, being much occupied with the lobster. 'The other one is a synthetic statement, something that involves the real world, so it's not like maths. A statement like "the tree is green" which may or may not be true depending on the time of year and so forth. Something that you need your senses to determine, like your eyes or your hearing.'

'Or your touch,' added Delroy.

'Yeah, I know what my senses are,' said the American.

'Good,' said Ayer, reclaiming the conversation and hoping it might, as soon as possible, progress. 'I'm sure you do. So to be succinct; the theory of Logical Positivism, and my particular version of Emotivism, claimed, some thirty years ago now, that all statements must fall into one of those two camps. Statements are assertions and assertions are like scientific facts – capable of being proved true or false. Verifiable if you will. If a statement is neither analytic nor synthetic, then it is without meaning because it is unverifiable. It is meaningless; mere noise or, some would say, merely an expression of emotion.'

The American lecturer looked deliberately blank. 'That sounds mighty clever,' she said with a little laugh. 'But, to be honest, it doesn't affect me. You know, I mean, so what? What you're saying is obvious.'

'What the Professor means,' said the Master, filling the embarrassed silence, 'is that if I were to say to you, "Murder is wrong," all I would be saying is, "I don't like murder."'

'Boo to murder or boo to adultery!' said Ayer. 'Where the thickness of my exclamation marks reveal the extent of my aversion. Nothing more, nothing less.'

'Boo to infidelity,' added Giles, glancing playfully at Delroy.

'Boo to blasphemy,' mouthed Cathy, locking the Dean in the eye.

'A lot of disapproval,' said the girl from Ohio. 'So let's get this straight, yeah. In case I don't understand – are you saying that morality doesn't exist, Professor?'

'Or God!' said Cathy and the Dean simultaneously.

'Or God?' echoed the American in mock horror. 'English liberals! You couldn't say that in my neck of the woods.'

'Luckily, we moved out of the woods some time ago,' said Ayer mildly. 'Now, if you don't mind, I would rather prefer we talked of something else. All this is very dull to my colleagues and increasingly dull to me.' He turned his attention away from her to address Giles. 'I was about to go back to Bertie. He's vociferous about Palestine, and wrote me a most amusing little card about religion and dragons. God! What a mind lies there!'

The conversation reverted to its islands of vicinity.

'So let me get this straight,' the American addressed herself to Cathy in a conspiratorial whisper. 'You're married to one of these guys?'

'Yes,' replied Cathy curtly. 'I am married to Francis Delroy who is seated just there to your left. The man over there is Lord Nicholas Giles sitting next to Professor Ayer. I am Catherine Delroy.'

'And I'm Mini Oglivy. Very pleased to meet you.' They shook hands, daintily, above the cut glass. 'My, aren't they just so clever? I mean all this analytic, synthetic stuff? Washes right over me, I'm afraid. In my world, good is good and bad is bad, and that's an end to the matter.'

Delroy, seated too far away from his own kind to have any fun, turned with a badly concealed sneer. He already knew he didn't like his wife. Within the next few seconds he'd added the American. There was something about her that he couldn't pin down.

'Good is good,' he leered over, pretending to find her attractive. 'That's a very big statement isn't it, Ohio? Can I call you that; for identification?'

'You can call me anything, so long as you call me!' She enjoyed the sense of the wife so near.

'My, what an offer!' Delroy let the sarcasm bulge in the sentence. 'I'll call you… darling. I'll call you. But back to your statement – your assertion. Good is good you say.'

'Well isn't it?'

'Don't know, darling. Let's see shall we? Name me something that's good.'

'God is good,' said Cathy with vehemence. 'God is perfect goodness.'

'Why not leave your precious God out of it just this once!' Delroy's acrimony was swift. 'I'll deal with your God when the Dean's listening, and kill you both with one stone. No, my dears,' he leant forward to have the two of them in his sights, 'I was thinking of something less superfluous than God. You know, something like "pleasure". Many people think that pleasure is good. I for example, I might say that pleasure is good.'

Mini Oglivy sniggered. 'I'd have to agree with you there.'

'I thought you would.' He lowered his glance. Maybe she was more fun than he thought.

'A group of philosophers called the Utilitarians thought that pleasure was good. Not just "kinda nice" in your speak, Ohio, but intrinsically, *per se* good. They identified good as pleasure and pleasure as good.'

Cathy was shaking her head as if she had a nervous tic. 'They were wrong then. There are plenty of things that are good besides pleasure. Virtue for one. And a good many pleasures are very bad for one. Habitual drunkenness being one.'

Delroy looked at her coldly. 'You would drive a saint to drink,' he remarked. 'But, predictably enough, you're missing the point. Can't you see, ladies, that it is logically incoherent to pretend you're defining a moral statement with a non-moral premise? Or, to put it more simply, pleasure, just isn't the same as goodness. It may feel like something good, it may contain something good, but it isn't *identical* with it. You can't reduce the word "goodness" to anything other than itself. That's what the great GE Moore said who graced this college when you were just a strand of DNA.' He leant back and stabbed half-heartedly at a slice of cold salmon. He rarely had much of an appetite these days. 'That's a cool necklace you're wearing, Ohio. What colour would you say it was?'

Mini Oglivy pressed it against her lips provocatively. 'Gee, well… it's yellow,' she said slowly, letting her eyes rest on him as cool as a predatory cat. 'A beautiful sunshiney yellow.'

'Very poetic.' Delroy's sneer played around his lips. 'Now try and define the colour.'

Mini giggled. 'My, you're such a tease, Mister Delroy. Why that's easy. Yellow's like the sun. Like daffodils and hot sand.'

'Not by analogy! A definition isn't an analogy!'

Good, he had taken her bait. She appeared to be confused for a fraction of a second and then said, 'Well – ah – well now, let me think. You want me to say what yellow is, without saying what it's like?'

'Yep.'

'It's…. it's a burning colour.'

'So is gold.'

'It's a hue or so darker than white on the spectrum. A mixture of green and blue.'

'No it isn't! Yellow's a primary colour,' Delroy was openly scathing now. 'And any scientist would know that was wrong.

White light is a mixture of all the colours of the
simply want you to define the colour yellow whi
unable to do. Do you give up?'

'Ah, weel. I guess I do, Mister Delroy. You ﹍
to surrender!' Damn! She'd overdone the drawl. But he didn ﹍
seem to be conscious. Only Cathy glanced at her with
something resembling surprise.

'You wouldn't be the first,' he said, openly eyeing her
cleavage.

'Moore said that just like the colour yellow, goodness is
impossible to define. It's just what it is; irreducible, perfect,
contained. And Moore thought we *recognise* it when we see it.
I certainly do. You're good, aren't you, Ohio? Very good
even?'

Mini pouted provocatively. 'I always do my best to be a
good li'l gal.' Cathy fiddled with the belt around her waist and
tried to ignore them both.

'To try to equate goodness with pleasure as Bentham did,
or duty as did Kant, or some God is to commit a fallacy –
the naturalistic fallacy.'

'The naturalistic phallus – ee? I've never heard it called
that before!' She laughed, pleased with her joke.

'I think your hormones are deceiving you, Ohio. I said
"fallacy". It's another word for a mistake, an error. Something
wrong.' Delroy glanced at his wife, thinking even she wouldn't
be this stupid. 'So Moore said that all philosophy was based
on a mistake, and our friend, the Professor here, went one
step further and said that any attempt at philosophical *truth*
is ridiculous, and that it's just a way of expressing your
feelings. And that had rather far reaching implications, as I'm
sure you can imagine.'

Mini nodded. 'But it's only his opinion – right?' She

ـ ⸮ked down the table to study the professor. 'I mean, for sure, he's a famous intellectual but his opinion's still only that. It's just his point of view.' At this, it was Delroy who looked at her sharply. Was she more clever than she let on?

'Had implications way beyond philosophy. Changed the way we thought about things. Structuralism and post-modernism arose from it. But hell! What's so great about those?' Weary now, Delroy poured himself another glass of Burgundy and lolled back in his seat. He switched his attention to his wife and calculated, once again, how much a divorce would cost. He had married her for the money which he'd drunk. But the proceeds of his book would be something. A divorce would cost him. Better to keep things the way they were. Still, he could have a little fun with the old thing in the meantime.

'You're looking very glamorous tonight,' he said insincerely.

Cathy blushed. 'Thank you.'

'Almost like you're ready for the real thing.'

'I'm sorry?'

'Like you're ready for the acronym of your precious proselytising society. She works for the Christian Order for Compassion and Knowledge ,' he explained in a slurred stage whisper to Mini. The drink was finally beginning to affect him. 'Never was a society less apt!'

'What are you saying?' Cathy was becoming puce; dangerously close to matching her gown. The plucked duck skin of her chest danced about in outrage.

'I'm saying you're a real pleasure to be with; a real pleasure.'

Mini – who had worked it out in a flash – held her hand to her mouth in horror. 'Oh my Lord,' she said, breathing quickly. 'Did you just say what I think you did?'

'He did,' said Cathy, straightening her back. 'And that's nothing new. You're a horrid, man. A drunk. A good for nothing.' This was hissed across the table but those closest to her were poking their food in embarrassment.

'At least I'm a happy drunk,' leered Delroy. 'Unlike you, you sewn up old bag!'

From the other end of the table Giles was picking up on the disturbance. He got up, between courses, and made his way down, placing an avuncular hand on his friend's shoulder. 'You all right, Francis? Seems you're having a less serene time down here than we are up there. Freddie's been regaling us with tales of his boxing friends. Do you know he's met the greats?'

'I don't care who the hell he's met!' When the drink in his bloodstream reached a certain saturation, Delroy was poison.

'Well you should!' Giles eyed him meaningfully as if to say, "Calm down. You're making an ass of yourself." 'You really should.'

Mini was eyeing Giles suspiciously. 'And this is Lord Giles?' she addressed her remarks to Cathy.

'Charmed!' said Giles, leaning over and kissing her hand.

'And you are a colleague of Dr Delroy? I mean, do you two collaborate on ree-search or something?' She was as certain as she could be that these two guys were "bi".

'I'm a historian and my colleague is an expert in French – culture and literature,' said Giles graciously. 'So we don't collaborate directly, though we meet in the impact of Baudelaire. Wouldn't you say, Francis?'

'*Hypocrite lecteur. Mon semblable, Mon frère*,' muttered Delroy into his bow tie.

'He's just explaining how the reader is worse than the

Devil himself, and for "reader" read audience, or even you yourself!' Giles' flow was effortless.

'I'm worse than the Devil?' Mini already knew exactly what had been said.

'Audiences in general, of which you are merely a particular example.' Giles was doing his best to get the conversation back to some level of restraint, but Delroy was having none of it.

'No... she is worse than the Devil!' he said, pointing inexactly at Mini. 'And she is the Devil, (aimed at his wife) and you are the Devil too, and I'm pleased to say it, because it's all just metaphysical tosh. Rubbish. Do you hear that? Everyone here? You're all idiots and I'm leaving this absurd congregation. Going to meet some proper people and have some proper fun.' He staggered to his feet but not before all three of the senior men around the table had risen to theirs.

'This is preposterous,' blustered the Dean. 'Are we to support such insolence at the dinner table? Really, Master, I do think he has gone too far.'

'I agree,' said the Master, drawing himself up to his full height, which was not great. 'You are a disgrace, Delroy. A disgrace to the profession, a disgrace to the college and, above all, a disgrace to yourself.'

Only Ayer remained calm. He simply regarded Delroy as he might have a tiresome student and scribbled something on a napkin that was passed to the offender. 'That's probably enough now old boy,' he said. 'Go and get yourself dried up, then come over to the guest room and we'll see if we can't solve this problem – won't be hard for a mind like yours.' Delroy saluted him with an unsteady toast, shoved the napkin in his pocket and staggered from the dais. Only one person in that company would ever see him alive again, and that was the person who ensured that no one else ever would.

* * *

'Taste's a funny thing, isn't it,' mused Giles. He was walking with Ayer as they ambled convivially down to the revellers on the Cam. The height of fashion was paraded before them in skirts that were so short they were more of a pelmet than anything else. Everywhere the emphasis was on slashed geometry; Vidal Sassoon haircuts and Mary Quant eyes.

'Explain!' said Ayer. 'I agree but I want to hear what constitutes "funny".'

'The wild fluctuations. The certainty of, say Digby over there, who I teach, that his flowered shirt goes well with a dinner jacket while I am equally certain that it does not. And the same is true of language. There's Francis at dinner, swearing like a trooper and making all sorts of unpleasant words float into the mind of his poor wife, while all the time it's just a matter of taste. Public taste. What's acceptable and what isn't.'

'I never knew you cared about his poor wife. Aren't you one of the reasons she's to be pitied, if indeed she is?'

'Perhaps! Though I think she was to be pitied before I ever came on the scene.'

Though Ayer was elderly now, he walked quickly and gave the impression that he was fundamentally alert. Giles had to stride to keep up with him. And when he spoke, Ayer had the sort of razor-sharp accent that gave the added, studied, precision of the elite. He was authoritative; you couldn't help but listen.

'I used to think that anything that couldn't be proved was meaningless, a mere noisy shouting match. But I mellowed over the years, Nick, as you will. And I came to agree more or less with those who assert that language is functional and prescriptive. So when I say "poor wife", or when you say "awful flowered shirt", we are *doing* something rather than just *saying* something. I am requiring you to agree that she is indeed a poor wife and you are requiring me to agree that all shirts festooned with flowers are hideous.'

'Well they are!' Giles laughed comfortably, pleased to have the great man to himself.

'We both know that. Of course they are, but the statement "flowered shirts are hideous" is still meaningless, just as meaningless as, "Delroy ought to behave better at dinner". I think he should, you think he should, but nothing in the world would make me say he *actually* should because it can't be demonstrated or proved. I'm merely wishing he would and inviting you to wish it too.'

Giles was studying the ground where a large area of pink ice cream, discarded by an elfin female, was an upcoming hazard.

'But when there's commonality?' he mused.

'When everyone in the world says the same thing, agrees the same thing? When everyone in the world says that fascism is despicable, doesn't it in reality become despicable? No, I'm afraid it does not. It still merely says, "I think fascism is despicable," though my friend, Hare, would agree with you and push you back into a world of universals and absolutes.'

'And yet of course things count,' Giles hummed softly to himself. 'Of course things matter.' Then, seeming to rouse himself, he glanced up, and seeing the helter-skelter, wrapped his arm through that of his old teacher.

152

'Hell's Bells look over there! That's an "absolute" if ever I saw one. An absolute must.' Giles had a quizzical, old-fashioned way of talking when he was really relaxed. He was far more à la mode with Delroy, but with the professor he could be truly himself.

'Come on, Freddie. Are you game?'

'You'll destroy me, Nick! You'll destroy me,' laughed the older man as they joined the queue for the rickety construction.

Aware that dons were in the queue, the drunken revellers stepped back a bit. 'Dr. Giles! Oh, go on, Sir, you'll enjoy it, you really will,' called some of his students encouragingly. They were unable to name the gentleman accompanying him who wore his trousers up to his ribcage, but they called out anyway in their well-watered way. 'And your friend will. You're never too old for this.'

'You be careful who you're calling old,' shouted Ayer over his shoulder, as he crouched down on the hessian sack. 'I'll be faster than the lot of you.' And with that he launched himself into space, felt the pull of gravity from the ground and not for the first time thought how very good it was to be alive.

* * *

It's at this point, or shortly afterwards, that an omniscient author, or ghost in the wings, would turn our attention back to Delroy, hunched and sitting on the edge of his bed. His tinnitus ears just possibly discerned a noise as the door to his "set" was pushed open. His spectacular unsteadiness might have caused him to fall as the earth came up to greet him. His tongue could have pushed itself into his throat – or it was helped to get there. Either way, surrounded by all the uncertainties of a post-modern landscape, Delroy's world was over. He no longer enjoyed the French intellectuals. He no longer enjoyed poached egg on toast. He no longer enjoyed Schoenberg because he no longer enjoyed anything. Delroy was dead, and his body a crumpled pile on the floor in Cecil Court with Wren's girls – Divinity, Law, Medicine and Logic looking down with neither pity nor scorn.

* * *

Shaz, the bedder, was surprisingly well behaved when she discovered him the next morning. She only let out one primal yelp of terror before scuttling off to alert the porter, and before long she was in her element, standing over the body, duster in hand, clucking and snuffling as if he were a fledgling fallen out of her nest.

'Ooh, he were a lovely man, the Doctor. I mean I knew 'im better than most, and 'e were always ever so nice to me. Brought me a bottle of brandy at Christmas 'e did. I knows there's some who thought 'e drank a bit too much and maybes 'e did, that's not for me to say like, but 'e were ever such a nice man. Don't you lays a finger on 'im, Mervyn. Not till the police arrive. Don't you touch 'im!'

By the time the police did arrive, she had assumed the aspect of a cat standing guard over its kill, and it was only with the utmost regret that she finally relinquished him to the authorities.

Detective Inspector John Moody, recently seconded from the Met., looked like the sharper type of bearded collie. This was fortunate since he owned one, and dogs and their masters have an unfailing familial resemblance. The dog's name was Blue, and it was he who ruffled helpfully through the dead

Delroy's pockets before ambling around the flat, sniffing in the manner of the idly curious. The pockets had revealed nothing more than a packet of Gauloise, a bunch of keys and a worn copy of *Les Fleurs du Mal*. The rest of the flat was similarly unrewarding.

'And you were the bedder here?' said Moody, addressing Shaz who had assumed the aspect of first centurion. 'Did the doctor always keep his room in such a mess?'

Shaz huffed up a bit. 'S'not a mess! It were always like this. 'E 'ated me touching 'is books and 'is papers. "Leave them!" he'd say. So I always did. Not my fault if it got a bit cluttered.'

The Inspector picked up a coffee mug with a month of mould growing inside, and a collection of cigarette stubs. 'Not a tidy man then?'

'Not really, I s'pose.'

'But a good man?'

Shaz sniggered. 'Well yeah, I guess so. Very popular if you get my meanin'.'

Blue had sauntered off down the stairs and was now standing on his back legs and sniffing the door. He barked in a casual sort of way and the Inspector went down.

'No sign of a forced entry. The lock is completely intact. Now isn't that interesting! What does that tell us, Blue?' The dog looked like it might cock its leg out of boredom.

'That tells us one thing. That whoever did for the doctor had a key — or was invited! Well that narrows it down a bit doesn't it, fella? Find out who that could be and we're pretty close to finding our culprit. If it's other than natural causes.'

They put a string of tape around the entrance to Delroy's staircase and called it a "potential crime scene". It was all a bit sad and had the feel of empty wine bottles and discarded glasses after the exuberance of the night before. The last revellers, returning home from their breakfasts, crunched the gravel and talked in hushed voices. 'Dr. Delroy's dead! Did you know him? Did he teach you?' Among the lecturers the mood was sombre, but no one could be quite sure whether to attribute that to the death, or the habitual surliness that follows a night of no sleep.

The Master made over a room to the detective and the porters gave him tea. He wanted to see just one person. The pleasantries were over quickly enough. The detective said that he was sorry for Mrs Delroy's loss. Cathy said that it was a great shock and the dog settled itself and prepared for the worst. He was committed to a two o'clock walk and was prepared to be quite difficult about it if his master ran over the time.

Cathy sat bolt upright with her handbag clenched on her lap, twisting unshaven legs together.

'Will you miss your husband, Ma'am?' The Inspector was known for coming to the point.

'No,' Cathy stared straight ahead. 'He was a drunk and a philanderer.'

The Inspector leaned back. 'So why didn't you divorce, if you don't mind me asking?'

Cathy steeled her back. 'The Gospel forbids it. "But I say to you Anyone who divorces his wife causes her to commit adultery" Matthew, Chapter 5; verse 32.'

'So you are religious. Does the Bible address bumping off?'

Cathy looked at him, unsmiling. 'The sixth commandment, "Do not murder",' she replied from a very great height. 'I thought everyone knew that.'

'And God's word is quite clear on the subject?'

'It is the revealed word of God. How could it not be

156

clear?' she answered. Her superiority riled the Inspector. He dug around in his brain to find remnants of his school Religious Studies, and then said 'The command to Abraham to sacrifice his son, the numerous acts of terror. Do these sit well with an all-loving God?'

Cathy leant forward, caught in the grip of faith. 'There are difficult passages,' she said. 'That need interpretation, obviously. But there are some things that are always wrong, and murder is one of those. Do not murder is an absolute. Full stop!'

'As clear today as in the Crusades, or the Inquisition or any one of the blood-filled centuries when Christianity ran amok?'

Cathy was not a bad woman. She was not stupid and she had moments of surprising clarity which visited her regularly when her faith was under attack. By great good fortune she had one now. 'You cannot confuse bad practice with bad belief,' she said, plumping herself up to warn off her foe. 'It is not the fault of God, that man is evil at root.'

She got the impression that the Inspector was looking at her closely and couldn't, for the life of her, guess what he would see. She very much hoped he would see a good, upstanding Christian; a fearless purveyor of the truth. But even the dog, which had embarked on an exhaustive study of its nether regions, was prone to a lack of respect.

The Inspector resumed. He seemed to be on to something. 'So God is good – but not man,' he said slowly. 'Only God is good. Do you believe that, Mrs Delroy?'

'I do.'

'God is the source of all goodness?'

'Indeed,' said Cathy with certainty. 'God is perfect goodness. Nothing exists without God.'

'And everything that God says is "good"?'

'Yes.'

'And how do we know what "He" says or commands? How do we apprehend it?'

Cathy was getting irritated. 'I've already told you, Inspector. Through Revelation; the Bible. Now if you don't mind, I have a meeting to attend.'

The Inspector leaned back in his chair and prepared to light a pipe. He packed the tobacco down and cleaned around the edge with a stained forefinger, eyeing her.

'So when the Bible says that anyone caught doing – let's face it – quite a number of things shall be put to death; that is what God would have done?'

Cathy nodded without hesitation 'Yes. God is Just. "I will punish the wicked for their sins"; Isaiah 13.'

'And the punisher would be exonerated, would in fact be doing *good*?'

Cathy hesitated for just a fraction too long. 'We would have to be very sure of God's pleasure,' she coughed a humourless laugh, and the Inspector felt his toes curl. She must have known of her husband's antics. They were common knowledge. Why couldn't he sympathise more?

'Can I go now,' she asked like an awkward child. He waved her away and watched her departure. Blue growled slightly as she neared his tail, but let her go without trouble. After all, he didn't want to endanger his master's timekeeping.

The Inspector noted the dog's reaction. Could this strident little person have killed? She had motivation certainly, the humiliation of the rejected, the "tyranny of the weak". But did she have murder in her? She didn't give the impression of madness, but when God whispers, who knows what He might say?

Blue was soon in a much better mood. He had a Kantian take on these things and thought that, once a promise was given, it had to be kept. His master and he had a contractual arrangement. If the policeman adhered to his side of the bargain, Blue was prepared to perform. He had long ago deduced that he was a "police dog" and, what's more, a "sniffer" and was proud of the position. A drugs haul in Peckham had been particularly noted.

So, it was just keeping to his side of the bargain when he bothered to report a smell as they crossed Old Court. Though faint, it was unmistakeable. He had smelt that smell before. He caught his master's eye.

'What is it, Blue? I've just taken you.' His master was always bad tempered when his blood sugar level was low. Still, there was no time to lose. He barked.

A taxi was drawing up, pulling slowly under the archway, and a woman was getting in. That smell! He was sure it was coming from her. Where had he smelt it before?

He barked again, more insistently this time. 'Come on, you spaniel,' he muttered. 'You'll miss her if you're not careful.'

'What is it, Blue?'

Blue lunged at the taxi and stood to attention, barking and wagging his tail. He had it! That was where he'd smelt it! The handle on the dead man's door. It was a distinctive, sickly smell that had made him, at once, take notice. And here it was again! On this woman, getting in to the car.

'Heathrow please. I've a plane to catch.'

'I'm afraid that won't be possible. At least not yet.'

Detective Inspector John Moody had been surprisingly obedient when it came to it. He had responded and was now between the smell and the open road. Blue stood himself down.

Mini Ogilvy removed one leg from the car.

'Why, Inspector, what do you want?' she asked with a radiant smile.

Another person was hurrying over, walking briskly, despite his years. A porter trundled attendance, carrying a crocodile suitcase with the initials AJA picked out in gold. Did Mini Ogilvy blanch when she saw him? The Inspector couldn't be sure.

'Is this taxi available?' Ayer had a waspish tone and glanced at his watch. 'I need to be in London for five. The Prime Minister is dining tonight.' The woman looked impressed.

'Why Professor Ayer,' she simpered. 'I remember what you taught me last night!'

The implication was undeniable and it alerted the Inspector. This was obviously Freddie Ayer. Should he detain him too? Somehow he didn't fancy the conversation they would have, but there was no doubt that the woman had meaning.

'Seems I am available,' grunted the taxi driver not bothering to get out, 'but you'll 'ave to 'urry up. Time's money and I've other calls, you know.'

Ayer acted quickly. He got into the back seat of the Citroen and said to the woman with the utmost suavity, 'If I have taught you anything it was entirely against my judgement.'

Then he leant forward and tapped.

'The station please.'

The taxi driver was upwardly mobile and didn't like being addressed as if he were of the lower orders.

'Oy,' he looked round in anger, 'don't you go tapping me like that, gov'nor. I'm not one of your 'ired 'ands! I'm not 'ere at your beck and call.'

Ayer was not the slightest discomposed. 'Forgive me,' he said smoothly. 'It's just that my family designed your car, and I need to be quick,' he added.

'What do you mean "designed me car"?' said the driver, still ruffled.

'My mother's family founded Citroen,' said Ayer disarmingly. 'But it really is no matter!'

The taxi driver's mouth gaped open. 'Blyme, gov'nor. So you're a Citroen?'

Ayer smiled. 'I suppose I am.'

'Well, in that case, come and sit up front with me, gov'nor. Come and ride in the cockpit. Bloody good car the Citroen, even though it is French.'

'Dutch originally!' they could hear, as the car made its way down the avenue, only impeded by a family of ducks.

The Inspector looked at Mini. 'A really important philosopher,' she said.

Back in the interviewing room, the Inspector puffed on his pipe. Mini breathed deeply. 'Gee, that smells good, Inspector.'

'You were at the dinner last night?' he asked as Mini twirled an earring. Her make-up was carefully done.

'Were you sitting anywhere near Dr. Delroy. The late Dr. Delroy, I should say.' He eyed her closely. She must know he was dead.

'Yeah, I was! Bang up against him.'

'And what did you make of him?'

161

'Well,' she arranged her high heels for symmetry, 'I thought he was okay.'

The Inspector puffed deeply and watched the circles of smoke drift upwards. He was debating in his mind how to proceed. She seemed open enough, didn't give the impression she had much to hide. But then, you could never be sure.

He took the plunge. 'Did you visit Dr. Delroy last night?'

Mini shook her hair, straightened her legs, and arranged them so she could survey them. So they could both survey them.

'No, of course not,' she said, eyeing him evenly. 'No Inspector. I did not.'

The Inspector stopped puffing. 'The last time you saw the Doctor was....?'

'At the dinner like everyone else.' She sighed and tapped her handbag. He noticed her nail was chipped. There was something..... just something. He glanced at Blue who was watching her, his head lying close to the floor.

He tried again. 'You had no dealings with Dr. Delroy?'

'Dealings? I've no idea what you mean. I didn't know the man beyond meeting him at dinner and he appeared to me absurd.'

'Absurd?'

'Yes, Inspector. Absurd!' She held his gaze, not blinking for a moment and for a split second the Detective saw something. But he had nothing to pin on her. He tried one last time.

'You found him absurd because…'

'It's not a crime, Inspector, to find a person absurd. He was meaningless – he led a meaningless life.'

'Well then, I'm sorry to have detained you,' he said feeling flattened and annoyed. There was nothing – he had to let her go.

Events happened quickly after that. The Inspector put a call through to his sergeant who was still hanging around in the morgue.

'You're not going to tell me it was natural causes?' said Moody. 'My day's been a complete waste of time!'

'It's still a bit ambiguous,' drawled the sergeant, 'but they seem to be saying "Yes".'

'Yes what?'

'Was natural causes,' repeated the sergeant.

'Blast! After all!'

'His blood was saturated with alcohol; and his liver fairly dissolved. Most probably organ failure. But they say they'll run more tests.'

'Blast!' said the Inspector again.

'There are strange marks on his body, and a thin line round his neck.'

'And there's no way of knowing?'

'We're not Dickson of Dock Green, are we, sir? The morgue report is inconclusive. We won't know for sure till the post-mortem's been carried out – and that won't be till Monday.'

The Inspector got to his feet, fed up with Ivory Towers. He made his way across the quad, keeping to the path, for it was only members of college who were allowed on the grass. Blue didn't stick to the rule.

At Heathrow, the flight to New York was boarding. Mini Ogilvy had the window seat and was opening her handbag. She fished inside and brought out a crumpled piece of paper with a damp patch in one corner.

'Murder is wrong' she read in Ayer's neat and regular hand. This was the note! The one he'd passed to Delroy. The one that gave her permission and that she'd taken from his corpse. She had always had a hunch that morality was void. Now she knew it, and the knowledge had made her free.

She put aside the heavy drawl, crossed her knees and relaxed. For the first time in her life, she knew with certainty that there was no such thing as a "wrong". And throughout the rest of her terrifying career as America's most dispassionate female killer, she stuck to her philosophical guns.

And although there was plenty of proof she had murdered – for she was eventually sent to Death Row – no one could ever prove that her actions were anything more than what society happened to dislike most.

* * * * * * * *

'**W**ell!' Chesterton let out a suppressed chuckle. 'She was a bit of a scallywag! That would be a case for my Father Brown, though I'd have to tone down the language.'

'I do not care for such things!' coughed Nietzsche who was holding on to his chair as if he might fall off it in excitement. The book had slipped from his grasp and now lay flat on the floor. 'Do you not see? Everything. Everything that I taught was present in that scene? Logical Positivism was the child I never fathered. It was the natural heir to my thought. And Ayer was an authentic genius. If only I had stayed sane and then perhaps I would have said those things myself!'

'But Ayer was suave and urbane,' said Chesterton innocently.

'I was suave and urbane!'

'You collapsed in the street when you were hugging a carthorse. You were too fussy to eat; that, at least, has been cured by death. Your language was the rant of a madman. My dear fellow, I could hardly call you urbane!'

'All right, all right! But why does that matter? The naturalistic fallacy as coined by Moore. I should have thought of that; for that is what I meant. I should have said it like that!'

'You couldn't! You were too preoccupied with yourself! But let's get back to the philosophy.' He bent down and retrieved the book that appeared to settle in his hand. ' Are we really to believe that Ayer is right? That there is nothing in morality that is greater than what an individual happens to like? I might like ham, while you might like murder. Is there nothing more to it than that?'

'Ham isn't a moral issue,' said the philosopher.

'It is if you're the pig,' retorted his companion.

Nietzsche ignored him. 'Yes Ayer is right. It's the obvious next step. If you can't prove a statement either true or false, it has no merit in it beyond one's own usage. It means that morality resides in individuals. It's what makes us essentially free!'

'Well that's a stupid idea,' said Chesterton, relighting the pipe and puffing, being careful not to create cinders. 'It's against common sense. And what's also against common sense is this "can't get an ought from an is" nonsense. Why can't you get an ought from an is?'

'Because they're different types of statement.' Nietzsche was impatient.

'I don't care if they're different types of bloody statement.' Chesterton was equally riled. 'If I see someone mugging an old lady, hitting her over the head while he runs off with her purse, which I suppose is the "is" bit of the statement, then I can say with perfect good sense, "Thief! You ought not to hit the old lady and run off with her purse," and so forth. To say that I can't, or ought not to, is utter madness! That's the trouble with you lot – you're all mad!'

'You cannot say it to remain logical. That's all Professor Moore was saying. It's not so difficult a thing! Or at least you can say it, but you can't prove it, and so there's no point in saying it, which is the point of Professor Ayer.'

The two men had reached yet another impasse. They were destined to be always at odds and sat there, seething, which was a shame as of late they had been getting on better. It was late in the day and they were both getting tired. Nietzsche was the next to speak.

'What do you say if we give up for the night? Retire to that inn over there? We could resume again in the morning. And we can put the book down for a while!'

Chesterton squinted. 'It might have spiders,' he said, eyeing the thatch with distrust. 'If you don't mind, I'll head for my former lodging in Fleet Street. It offers some very good ale. And there's no question of you having this.' He patted the book conspiratorially. 'We're not having you run amok! There's no telling what you would do! No, no my friend I'll have the book while you find a nice place to sleep. You might be lucky and get a straw mattress. At the very least, they might wash your socks!'

'There's nothing wrong with my socks!' shrieked the philosopher at the departing mass of Chesterton's shoulders. 'To say I thought you were the Übermensch. I've learned how wrong I can be!' He hurried across the pathway and ducked his head under the porch. 'Have you a bed for the night?' he asked politely, but of course the landlady could neither see nor hear him, so he settled himself near the fire and pulled off his socks. Sniffing them cautiously he hung them as close as possible to the flames to dry out. Before long, and quite without reason, most people had moved to the other bar, and the landlady was looking in the phone book for an emergency pest control number.

'It's the strangest of smells,' she explained into the phone. 'I've never smelt the likes of it before. No I don't think it is rats but I suppose it might be. Yes, if you could. In an hour?'

***

They met again in the morning. The philosopher looking quite rested with a pair of very dry socks, while Chesterton appeared somewhat the worst for wear. The book sat upright in his pocket.

'Don't ask! You know what journalists are like,' was all he was prepared to say.

Nietzsche was smug. 'Nobody could see me. I had a very good sleep.'

'I met a friend,' said Chesterton. 'Charlie Lyons. Former colleague, editor of 'The Burlington Gazette'. He's having a rare old time. I'm due to meet him again in the future.'

'He is dead?'

'Oh yes, quite dead. And much the better for it. Very much more mellow and fun. There had been a party and they left the wine out. Well, it wasn't there for long, if you get my drift, old fellow! Now, who's on the menu today? I can't quite remember everyone who was part of the Sage Train. Was there anyone you'd particularly like to see?' He fished out the book and it opened obligingly, falling straight to the page with the index.

'I had my turn yesterday,' admitted Nietzsche, surprising himself as he said it. 'But that's good of you, my friend. *Verr gut!* I propose that we read another quite neutral, but someone who relates to what we spoke of yesterday. For if you remember, we were much concerned with the thought that our morals are quite of our choosing. And not only our morals but morality itself!'

'Ah yes!' said Chesterton rubbing his head and rummaging in his knapsack for bicarbonate of soda. 'Excellent when you're a little bit dicey,' he explained. 'Yes – all that business. We couldn't agree about that.'

The book's pages turned in the wind until they came to rest and lay open. 'Does it have a plan?' asked the philosopher, glaring at the leaves querulously as they rustled about. He didn't like giving the book any status. But Chesterton needed no prompting.

'Seventeenth century London!' he announced with triumph. 'And back into Fleet Street and my own stomping ground. Funny when I've just come from there! I must keep an eye out and see if Charlie's still there – hair of the dog and all that! Thank you!' He patted the book again like an old friend and replaced it in his pocket. Nietzsche glared and glowered. He had no time for talking with books.

* * * * * * * *

London 1668

Thomas Hobbes

'The Black Eagle it shall be then.'

Thomas Hobbes ducked though the doorway with Aubrey close on his heels. The tables nearest the windows were well lit but further back candles burned, even though it was half ten in the morning. They had to shout, mouthing to each other to press on and make for one of the furthest rooms. But, as they pushed, a young man stood up.

'I'm just away,' he said, in the warm tones of a Wiltshire man. 'Shall I leave the Broadsheet or hang it?'

'Hang it if you will. There'll be others to savour it. We've no time to read today.' The youth inclined his head and edged his way between table and settle to let the gentlemen through. He disappeared in a cloud of tobacco and the heightened tones of debate.

Hobbes took his place with some speed. He was taller than his companion and, though in his eightieth year, moved with ease. Aubrey seated himself opposite. The boy came over for their pennies; a dirty napkin slung over one arm.

'Two cups of coffee and a pastry,' said Hobbes, handing over the coins. Aubrey thanked him.

'This place did well to survive,' muttered Hobbes, removing a fur-lined coat. 'The fire stopped just east of here. Did you see the ruins?'

'I did,' responded his companion with the enthusiasm of a countryman who had only heard of the Great Fire from others. 'Your own house survived?'

'Ay. We were blessed, though I was in Derbyshire at the time.'

Aubrey nodded; Hobbes' friendship with the Duke of Devonshire was famous. As was his familiarity with the king whom he had tutored as a boy, and whose protection he now enjoyed.

'His Majesty raised his hat to you most warmly just now from his coach.'

'Ay,' said Hobbes, looking around. 'But don't speak it too loudly. His priests don't like me at all. The dogs are more vicious than the master when they bark on the latter's behalf!'

His companion laughed. Though Thomas Hobbes was renowned for his intellectual ferocity, there was a timidity about the man in person. Indeed, he'd often heard Hobbes joke that his mother had given birth to twins; himself and fear. The philosopher would have nothing to fear from him though. Growing in his mind was a book he planned to write – brief biographies of the most notable men in the land – and Hobbes was one to include. Aubrey was here to renew the friendship but he was also here to make notes.

The coffee arrived in china cups; steaming, viscous and black.

The younger man took a sip and winced. He would have preferred chocolate but he needed his wits about him to converse with a political philosopher, and the black stuff was noted for that.

'You look remarkably well, sir.'

'I am remarkably well, considering,' replied Hobbes,

stirring the liquid. 'I find these past eight years more suited to my temperament than Cromwell's mob. You know I value authority, be it a king or a parliament, but it's good to see the former restored.'

Aubrey strained to hear him, for the noise was very great. He cupped his hand behind his ear and said, 'What?'

'I said it's good to have Majesty restored,' repeated Hobbes.

'Oh ay, that it is,' Aubrey smiled, cursing himself for forgetting how softly the philosopher spoke. The man conversed almost in a whisper, holding his hand above his mouth, as if he to deflect his words. They should have met elsewhere. But then some men to their left got up, and everyone stood to let them through.

'That's a little better,' he said. 'Now I can hear what you say.'

'What do you want me to say?' Hobbes retorted, suddenly aware that the meeting had a secondary purpose.

'What I want and what I will get are different items, sir. I'll be honest. I plan to write a small compendium. I wish to feature you and require some knowledge of your philosophy. Just a little, enough to fill a tea cup if you will.'

'You could read my works. *Leviathan* is everywhere in print.'

'Ah! I have, I have!' replied Aubrey soothingly. 'A very great work and *De Cive* too, albeit in Latin. But works do not replace what is said in broad speech.' He smiled.

Hobbes was still wary.

'You know I have a horror of my words being wronged. Taken out of their place. I had to burn my papers when the authorities examined them. I have no wish for my body to go the same way!'

'Forsooth, sir, you will not be burned. We have come a long way from burning.'

'Not long enough,' replied Hobbes, who had been born when Elizabeth was still on the throne, and whose grandma had witnessed men go to the stake and had regaled him with tales of the horror, while she sat and sewed and he learned his grammar. 'Not long enough. When do you plan to publish?'

'Long after your days, sir,' Aubrey replied, doing a quick arithmetic in his head and concluding that, despite appearances to the contrary, Thomas Hobbes could not live forever.

'Very well,' Hobbes bit into his pastry. "Goose flesh skin," his companion noted. "Wide pores. Close shaven apart from a tuft beneath the lip. Eyes mostly hidden, except when excited, which then grow big and round."

'Very well,' said Hobbes again. 'You can speak to Warren!'

Warren was his amanuensis, and former baker for the Devonshire estate. He went everywhere with Hobbes and wrote for him when the former's hand shook with palsy. It was said that he slept with him at night for Hobbes was afeard of the sprites. Aubrey did not believe the rumour, though he would afterwards make sure that it lived.

'I plan to,' he said. 'But Warren is not your good self. I understand a little of your thinking, and have a thirst for more.'

'Aristotle was a fool,' Hobbes launched, putting both elbows on the table, leaning over and speaking clearly as if to emphasise that in such matters he was not afraid. 'A pagan mind mistaken. All this nonsense about virtue arising from the polis, how men could live harmoniously if they seek the common good. Tosh, sir! The opposite is true. Look around you.' He waved his arm and Aubrey followed his gaze. The coffee shop was steaming, everywhere men bent towards each other, embroiled in hot debate.

'It looks fully gracious to me,' Aubrey ventured.

'But what lies underneath?' Hobbes leant back.

'More civility, yet to be unearthed?'

'If you believe that, we have nothing in common,' retorted the philosopher, as he called the boy for more coffee. 'Men are everywhere brutal and this appearance is all but show. Each one of them is hiding his true nature. What's your most prized possession, sir?'

Aubrey considered. He was in the process of losing all his estates in a series of unpleasant lawsuits.

'My home,' he replied. 'Though I fear I may not always possess it.'

'Because men seek to remove it?'

'That they do.'

'Exactly,' said Hobbes. 'My point exactly. Men cannot do other than seek their own advantage. T'is their nature! These people here would trample on each other as freely as stampeding beasts if they were permitted, and it gained them a return. T'is human instinct, sir! We are all beasts at heart.'

'Forgive me if I say, that that seems a mite uncharitable!'

The philosopher was not offended. 'On the contrary. I have a great respect for the human being,' he parried. 'And that respect shows me his motivation. His push and pull; what drives him. Man has two forces at work. A dark side as well as a fair. In a state of nature the dark would win. Neither rules, nor order, nor justice there would be, but everywhere man against man. Without authority, it would be one over another, gained by force and fraud.'

Aubrey nodded, thinking of a particularly unpleasant letter he had just received from an assailant to whom he owed money.

'As you said, sir, in words that are already famed, "Without laws all around us is fear and the danger of violent death. And the life of man, solitary, poor, nasty, brutish and short."'

Hobbes smiled, pleased with the recognition. They chatted on, and after a while he felt for his fob watch, an article he'd not consulted since they'd arrived, but of which he now had need. Dinner was served at eleven thirty prompt in his parlour, and though he was pleased to talk, Warren must not be kept waiting. Not finding the watch, he stood and swatted his clothes abruptly.

Aubrey stood too.

'What ails you, sir?'

Hobbes didn't reply, but concentrated on the search.

'What ails you?' Aubrey asked again, trying not to smile; the philosopher's wig had loosened and now hung askew on his head.

'My timepiece!' said Hobbes, bending down to inspect the sawdust on the floor.

'You are sure you had it this morning?'

'I did!'

'And you do not have it now?'

'I do not! The chain is here, see!' And Hobbes held up the silver chain which was still attached to a strap held under the shirt.

They stared at the chain which dangled in his hand like a body without its feet.

'It's been cut,' said the philosopher inspecting the last link 'Look, sir, here! Can you see the sharp mark of tool?

Whoever did this was quick. I felt nothing. Neither pull nor cut. Damn it! The thing was new this year!'

They looked around, but the faces nearby were occupied and innocent. Everywhere debate flowed, unchecked by clandestine guilt.

'By Gad what to do...' Hobbes began again and then sat down abruptly. 'It was here!' he said at last, glancing around as he spoke. 'Here. At this table. You remember, sir? That man who gave me his seat. The Wiltshire boy. Sure as the day!'

Aubrey said nothing. 'What will you do, sir? Will you pursue him?'

'No,' muttered Hobbes, furtively. 'I wouldn't dare.'

'I dare say your watch will reappear,' soothed Aubrey, fighting down the desire to chuckle. He couldn't say why he was amused. But he was and there was no denying it. It had something to do with the old fellow's sense of outrage. As if Hobbes, friend of duke and king, could be radically hurt by the loss of a watch when there was a rich house for him to go home to and a coffer full of plate. Aubrey had the notion that some men had less right to complain than others, and being on the point of losing most of his own capital, he classed himself among the latter. He could recall the young Wiltshire lad with his shock of hair and rugged, honest face. 'Oh well,' he thought, how looks will deceive us. 'And how passing strange that naughtiness can be so very well hid.'

* * *

'I must report it and you're the witness,' mumbled Hobbes as he hailed one of the Hackney coaches that could now be hired at the Strand. The horse was clapped out, so it was Aubrey's turn to fear for a wasted hour.

'Is it far, this place of yours?' he asked as they settled themselves in and pulled the cloth over their knees.

'Not far,' replied Hobbes. 'I'm surprised you haven't been there afore. It's one of the sights of London.' Aubrey sighed and resigned himself to the certainty that his dinner would be late and that the afternoon's appointments would now all be missed.

'Why don't you just call a Beagle?' he asked as they sped along.

Hobbes glanced at him but didn't bother to reply.

The courthouse, where they were dropped off, had all the customary offices and high ceilinged rooms. It had staircases and porticos and a vestibule where they left their canes; in short, it had nothing of poverty or degradation about it, but spoke of authority in its most regal and imposing form. The servant who took their cards steered them well away from the common crowd as he showed them into the office of the clerk. The man nodded gravely, took a description of the Wiltshire lad and promised he would pay his best boy to solve the case. 'Any distinguishing marks?' he asked, quill poised.

Hobbes shook his head, 'Average stature, seemly countenance, affable; dangerous. I fear he'll be back for more. Pay one of your men to hang around the Black Eagle for a day or so and protect good citizens from a rogue.'

'We will do our best to catch him,' the clerk said as he closed the ledger. 'And I dare say we'll have success. We often do. Can you stay to hear a case or two, gentlemen? There's still trials to be heard this session.'

The courthouse was peculiar in having only three sides.

The fourth being directly open to the street and thronged with common folk, pushing to hear the fun.

'It must be darn cold in winter,' remarked Aubrey to the man. He was more interested now than before.

'Guards against prison fever, sir. Lets the clean air in and black air out.'

Hobbes fussed and muttered that the air must be very black if it forced a building to go without a wall but his humour was lost on the clerk, who was occupied in pushing them to the front.

'Why does he care where we sit?' wondered Aubrey. 'Is our status so apparent that he should bother so?' He remarked as much to the philosopher, saying that Hobbes must be much renowned, if even an obscure clerk fawned after him. But the philosopher replied with a taut look.

'My *purse* wasn't stolen, just my timepiece,' he remarked significantly, and left Aubrey to wonder how much he'd handed over to catch the thief, and how much more the clerk could expect. He also wondered, as a vague misgiving at the back of his mind, what safeguards were in place to make sure that the Wiltshire lad was indeed the culprit. And how any trial that came of it would be guaranteed fair? But, by then, the man had pushed through the throng, arranged two gilt chairs to be positioned right beneath Mr Magistrate, and John Aubrey put such qualms to one side.

'T'is a crowd puller,' the man informed them, as they looked about wonderingly at the heightened clamour and the jeering. All the prisoners were arrayed in the dock, so there was no telling whose case was next, until a bailiff grabbed a woman and pulled her roughly to the front.

She was a poor thing of about fifty with drab ringlets, a dirty bonnet and a plunging neckline on what was probably her only dress. She pulled a flimsy shawl around herself and leant on one hip, staring around at where the jurors sat.

'What is your plea?' intoned the bailiff. But the woman continued to stand there, tweaking at the shawl and picking her nose.

'You must put forward a plea. What is your plea?' repeated the bailiff. The woman appeared dazed and it was only after an age of jeering that she eventually replied, 'Not guilty,' in a cracked, cockney voice.

The clerk winked at the gentlemen. 'Just listen to this,' he whispered. 'Never in a Christian country was there the likes of such a charge! You'll thank me,' he added, standing on his toes to get a better view.

The magistrate read the charge so slowly, and with so much disdain, that even the worst of the crowd felt satisfied.

'Martha Holmday,' he said. `You are charged that, on the fourteenth of December last, a woman in the room next to yours, who has, on occasion, seen your activities through a hole in the wall and has seen, on diverse occasions, various vagabonds and ruffians follow you in to your room, where you have entertained them in such manner not befitting a Christian woman. On fourteenth December last, this maid, who was living in the room next, heard a commotion and putting her eye to the hole, saw a small dog fawning about your person. Whereupon, with this said dog, you did much misuse him, causing him to abuse you in a gross violation of nature. Whereby a charge of a beastly and pernicious wrongdoing is brought before you this day.'

The crowd howled in delight, while the woman looked around; indignant, half simple and alone.

'I never did. I knows not what you say! That woman you talk of, the one that says she's seed that. She wrongs me!

She would say anything 'bout me! She would. I don't know no dog.'

The magistrate swatted at her protest.

'It has been suggested,' he droned, luxuriating in the continuing appreciation of the mob, 'That the dog be brought in. A mongrel it is. And if said creature knows you, then there is something in the charge. If he does not, well, then, maybe there is less of a case.'

'So the dog becomes the law?' Aubrey whispered to Hobbes, not wishing to break the elder's rapt attention.

'It seems that way,' he hissed back. 'But better a dog's law than no law at all!'

The dog was brought in, a cheerful little mongrel with a long tail and friendly demeanour. He wagged his tail and panted and looked very appreciative of all the fuss and attention as he was trotted to and fro across the court. The woman appeared to shy away. She was frightened of him, and when he was brought up close and lifted so as to be at the same height as her, and the hairy thing pulled his ears back and gave her a friendly lick, she paled.

'He knows her! He knows her!' screamed the crowd. 'Look! See! He even tries to kiss her! He knows her – in more ways than a good dog should!'

'Maybe she gave him a bone,' suggested a female voice from somewhere.

'Maybe he gave her a bone!' screamed a wit from the sidelines, and the crowd howled in delight, banging their sticks on the floor and stomping with glee.

The woman hung her head.

Her husband was brought in, a large rump of a man who had nothing with which to protect his wife, neither character nor money. Despite his size there was no weight behind him and, if anything, his blackguard looks only made matters worse. He was obviously not to be trusted, so when he explained that the dog belonged to a neighbour and his wife commonly fed it and that was why it recognised her, he was jeered at. Even Aubrey had to smile, despite feeling sorry for the wretch. Hobbes stared straight ahead, startled by the power of the crowd.

It took no time at all for the case to be finished and the jury to withdraw to decide the fate, not only of this woman, but of everyone who stood in the dock.

'T'is a capital charge,' Hobbes volunteered. 'If they pronounce, she'll hang.'

Aubrey glanced at him. Even though the philosopher was a nervous man, on this occasion, Hobbes' anxiety was entirely to do with the noise.

'Do you fear death?' he asked in a normal voice, for now that the jury had withdrawn, conversation could be resumed.

'I do, but look upon it as my last great leap in the dark,' replied the philosopher, crossing his legs to reveal a pair of fine woven stockings. 'Every man fears death, and would do anything at all to avoid it.'

'I disagree!' Aubrey was surprised by the clarity of his own reaction. 'Men fear many things more than death. Loss of principle being one of them. Why does a hero stand up for a principle when the cost of so doing is death? I'll tell you why! He calculates it a price worth paying for what he believes to be true.'

'There are not many heroes,' replied Hobbes acidly. 'Besides, I talk of the crowd. People like this…' He glanced around. 'Death and the fear of death is everywhere here. It's what they've all come to see!'

Aubrey said nothing and allowed the philosopher to

continue. 'Now, given that fear, which stalks them and us too, my friend, Society makes an arrangement and surrenders to another – monarch or parliament – the right to restrict our lives. Society allows itself to be governed. The only thing it demands in return is that its citizens are protected; allowed to keep their lives, their safety, with their possessions protected too.'

'A sort of contract?' said Aubrey, thinking of the supercilious magistrate they had just seen and the reasons he was tolerated.

'Exactly!' said Hobbes, 'A social contract by which we live. The monarch is beyond it. He can make or break a law at will and be above the law, so long as he protects his people. Once he fails, the mob is justified in rising. They can replace him with one that will.'

'Authority is above the law?' Aubrey scowled, instinctively disliking the thought.

'Ay, authority may be above it, if it befits the common good. Authority is as important as justice. It's authority that keeps us safe.'

'So everything comes down to order,' said Aubrey eyeing the woman still in the dock. 'And all principle can be surrendered, if it will keep us safe?'

'We are mere machines,' said Hobbes, standing to leave, 'And all our thoughts are dictated by previous events. That woman there is innocent, even if she did have dealings with a dog!'

'Now you've confused me!' replied Aubrey, also rising and pulling on his coat, aware that he was free, unlike the wretch in the dock. 'Surely she's either guilty or not? How can she be innocent if she did perform the act, which I doubt,' he added as an afterthought.

'You're forgetting the chain of events,' said Hobbes cryptically. 'Consider the circumstances that caused her to act in such a way. Each leading to the next. She's a cog, a mere component in the perpetual movement of cause and effect that makes up a human life. We all are, sir. It is that certainty that frightens me most.'

They were halfway up the street when they heard the roar from the courtroom. It could only mean one thing. That the magistrate had donned the black cap and the woman been sentenced for a crime she'd probably not committed, quite apart from whether it was a hanging offence. Aubrey could only imagine being powerless in a system so much greater than oneself.

'So society acts out of fear of that,' he mused, 'By which I mean death and the stripping of possession.'

'And of fear of life without that,' replied Hobbes seamlessly. 'The final sanction by which all else is saved.'

They parted outside Hobbes' home in Fetter Lane. As Aubrey shook the old man's hand, he thought how much more cogent and robust he was than he had earlier credited. There was something noble in his attempt to look reality in the face, even while his hand shook and he started at every loud sound. Hobbes was more a man than Aubrey had remembered. It might be a strange way of seeing reality, but it had something compelling about it.

He had not gone a hundred yards up the road, walking quickly now to try and save the remnants of the day, eat a quick lunch and get to the meetings, when he heard a shout behind him. It was Hobbes, trotting along on the open flags, lifting his legs, to avoid the gutter.

'John,' he called. ' John Aubrey. Stop, sir! Stop!'

'Mr Hobbes! How can I help you?'

'I've found it!' said the philosopher, chuckling like a schoolboy. 'Warren's fault of course. He'd fastened the chain without the timepiece when he'd taken it off to be oiled. T'was not cut.'

'Well then, I'm glad of it, sir! A relief to you, no doubt.'

'Considerable,' replied the philosopher. 'Though I know in my mind that men are ruthless, it sickens me when I prove my own case. Despite my philosophy, John, I would prefer to imagine a world with good men rather than bad.'

'I thought that lad looked innocent,' replied Aubrey. 'He had no air of malice about him. He didn't look like a cut purse at all.'

'Looks can be deceiving, but yes, you're right. Will you hail me a cab when you get to the corner?'

'You're returning to the magistrate?'

'I'm returning to the magistrate. There is no pleasure in pursuing an innocent man, even when I've handed over a purse.'

'No, indeed. So you see, sir, justice is not arbitrary, for if it was, you would let the matter be!'

Hobbes eyed him without speaking. Finally he replied. 'I'm not sure you fully understood me.'

'No, sir. I agree. I'm not sure I fully understood you.'

'I was saying,' began the philosopher, and then held up his hands and laughed in a way that was both dismissive and let them each off the hook.

'No matter. Read *Leviathan* if you wish to follow me more clearly. For despite your claims to have done so, I see no signs of the event! I never implied that justice was arbitrary – far from it. Justice is the currency of the people; it is the authority that oversees it that's more changeable!'

'If authority is arbitrary, it cannot come from God. So

then there's no Divine Right of Kings,' Aubrey said, teasingly, for he knew how Hobbes hated that particular subject, and how he was rumoured to believe it.

But the philosopher was not to be drawn. He had enough good sense to detect a real danger from an imagined one. And his stomach was rumbling. He smiled, his old face suddenly lighter, tapped the younger man on the shoulder and said, 'Well, that's a matter for His Majesty to decide. Where authority comes from is not my concern, only why we tolerate it!'

He turned and they went their separate ways. Each to their dinners and their different days. Meanwhile, the fair-haired Wiltshire lad handled the cudgel he kept in his jacket pocket and waited in a lane near the Black Eagle Coffee House. He didn't know how long he must wait before a frail one would emerge. He'd bide his time. Someone would come; sauntering out into the late summer sun, suspecting nothing with a full belly and a buzzing head. This was where a certain class of people came. Talkers were always the least observant, especially if they recognised him as a customer of the place. It had worked in the past; it would work again. And meanwhile, he could wait.

* * * * * * * *

'**B**ut it's all so depressing!' Chesterton got up from his chair and stomped about, swiping at a daisy with his walking cane. He regretted the action immediately because he had damaged a well-meaning plant.

'It is not!' said the Professor, also getting up. 'It is *gut.*'

'No, it's depressing. That view of things. The idea that we're all seething barbarians held in check by fear. I'm not held in check by fear – I just don't want to hurt things, or murder or steal. I don't have it in me, you know.'

Nietzsche wrinkled his nose to look scornful. 'You do. You've just submerged it. It's buried so far in your subconscious you can't even feel it!'

'You don't *know* about the subconscious. Freud came after you!'

'He did not! Well… yes… all right… but I influenced Freud. And I was ten leaps ahead of him! Of course you have an unconscious mind, and everything you don't like, or are ashamed of, you straight away put into there! Your dreams are those thoughts climbing out.'

'But I have nice dreams,' said Chesterton lamely. 'And what of poor old Hobbes with his theory of a social contract? It makes sense but it's so damned bleak. I want to stand up for good natures and say that, in every one of us, there is perhaps a push and pull. A part of us that wants to get on – and we'll trample on others to get there. But another part that is sometimes prepared to put the other first, not because we love them, but because they count! There are many who are less pessimistic than Hobbes. Hume for example. He saw the benevolence in man. You'll notice I've put God to one side!'

'WHY?' Nietzsche turned round with sudden force. 'Why are you leaving God out? Religion is the ultimate social contract, the one that you all obey. You try to please your God, tiptoeing around to please him. Don't you see that you follow a madman? What God is vile to his creatures, taunts Abraham with killing his son, or bothers what people should wear? Don't you know that the Jews are prevented from mixing two types of fabric? What are you wearing – cotton and wool? Well you!' He stabbed the air with one finger, 'Yes you are a sinner! For you have broken one of the six hundred and thirteen – YES – six hundred and thirteen commandments. And you call me mad!' he puffed.

'It's not like that.'

'What's that you say? Speak up, man, I can't hear you.'

'I said it's not like that!' said Chesterton more loudly. 'That's such a superficial assessment. Designed to ridicule and pervert. It completely misses the point. Faith is not about fear; it is always much deeper than that!'

'Faith is nothing but cowardice. The belief of one who's afraid. Man invented the Other to stop himself being alone. Faith has no hold over brave men. It's only the cowards it holds.'

'Well, that's simply not true!' asserted Chesterton feeling the book move in his pocket. 'Faith does not prevent a man from feeling fear, or courage or bewilderment. It is an adjunct that runs beside a life – it does not detract from the struggle. Faith doesn't take away fear, neither does it arise from it.'

'Show me,' snarled the philosopher. 'Show me a God-botherer who does not feel fear.'

'Very well,' said Chesterton, taking off his hat. 'It would be my honour.' He opened the pages which were hot to the touch, so keen was the book to be opened. It fell immediately at a chapter towards the end. Chesterton couldn't help but notice that there were fragments of powdered glass caught in the binding. They shone and reflected the sunlight. And Nietzsche had already seen them.

* * * * * * * *

AMSTERDAM JULY 27 1656

Baruch Spinoza

The rabbi pulled the prayer shawl over his head, and all around the crowded synagogue, the honourable hakhams and elders did the same. Their faces were hidden but grave, for this was a moment of the deepest solemnity.

The chief rabbi took his place on the bimah, towards which all the pews faced and looked at the young man standing beneath him. Espinoza appeared untouched. He looked to neither right nor left, though the entire community was present; people he had always known.

Rabbi Morteira cleared his throat; a deep "ahem", which did cause the young man to look up. The rabbi sought his eyes, willing him to raise a hand to stop the business there and then. This was possible right to the last minute. A single, solitary sign to say that the nonsense was over; that was all it would take. Then he, the rabbi, could come down from the platform. He could walk over and embrace him. He could wipe the tears from his eyes and invite him to recant, and the whole assembly would cluster round, relieved to have him back. The lessons could resume, the study of the Torah where the young man showed such brilliance. And who knows the ways of the Lord, maybe one day his successor? But here Rabbi Morteira stopped his musing, for he had found his pupil's eyes and their calm told him everything he did not wish to know.

"Are you sure?" he wanted to ask. He also wanted to ask, "Why?"

But instead, he asked neither. He opened the printed prayer book and turned to a page he had never used before and started to read in a deep, solemn voice so that the whole place reverberated with the awful words.

'By decree of the angels and by the command of the holy men, we excommunicate, expel, curse and damn Baruch de Espinoza. Cursed be he by day and cursed be he by night; cursed be he when he lies down and cursed be he when he rises. Cursed be he when he goes out and cursed be he when he comes in. The Lord will not spare him, but then the anger of the Lord and his jealousy shall smoke against that man, and all the curses that are written in this book shall lie upon him, and the Lord shall blot out his name from under Heaven.'

The curse thundered on, as harsh as any flogging, for as every new pronouncement fell, it stripped him to the core. By the time the thing was completed, Baruch had lost all – everything; from a place in Heaven to permission to speak. He was lost, cast out of the community, from sanctity, comfort and ease; everything, in short, which the world holds dear.

But Rabbi Morteira had not yet finished.

'Is there anything you wish to say?' he asked, with the deep, sonorous voice which Baruch had loved, even when he had questioned the "truths" it was used to impart.

He looked up and the buzz of the crowd drained away like sand in an hour glass. Everyone strained to hear him.

'This does not force me to do anything I would not have done of my own free will, had I not wished to spare us the scandal. I cannot be a teacher of philosophy without also being a disturber of the peace.'

He didn't lift the prayer shawl until he was well out of the doors. He would not do that to them, wouldn't dishonour the place they held most dear. There were no goodbyes to be said, the ones that mattered having been done the night before. So, he pushed his handcart down the narrow streets of the Jewish quarter in old Amsterdam, nodding to one or two Christian acquaintances that lived around, for this was no ghetto but a prosperous part of town. The painter, Rembrandt, had his home here but Baruch did not see him, either through the window or out on the street. Maybe he was abroad in the warm summer day.

He walked on, sleeping in ditches or in the lee of the great windmills that were everywhere dotted around. He loved to hear the swish and hum of their sails powered by the wind alone. He breathed and loved the God who made them, who lived in the air that moved them, that kept him and all else alive. No edict could dispel that, or make him downhearted. It mattered not that he had no money and only the clothes on his back, and a few others stuffed in the trunk that was just now belted down in the cart. He had some books and his quills and ink. He had an etching of the mother he could barely remember, and some precious metals left from the trading house he had run with his brother.

'Sell them,' the latter had said, when they had parted for the last time.

'You never know, they might save you one day. You're a fool! Why throw all this away when all you have to do is conform?' His brother had asked the question, gesturing round at the stones they had purchased, lying in trays for resale. He had scooped out one or two of the smaller and wrapped them in a cloth for Baruch. It seemed the least he could do.

Spinoza looked at the cloth and remembered how his

brother had tied it. Fiercely, like lashing something tight in a storm. He undid it, rolled out the glittering things and tossed them into the wind. The grasses immediately covered them. Then he picked up the arms of the handcart, and slowly went on his way.

* * *

Rijnsburg: Four years later

His table was under the window, next to the lathe, to get the best light for his work. It was early morning and Baruch was up with first light. He picked up the glass and inspected last night's work, assessing the way the lens was taking shape; curved, though not yet enough to be finished. It was a transformation – turning a piece of glass into a lens for specula or optascope. And hard work, grinding away with ever smaller granules, until the shape had been assumed and the emery polishing begun.

For some reason, Baruch did not sit straight down but made for the door, throwing it open to greet the day and view the village below. It was a fine morning, with the sun creeping up beyond leagues of flat earth with their dykes and ditches, over which the mist still hung. The village was stirring, and beneath his landing, pigs were being driven, none too expertly as it turned out. Little Jans waved up at the lens grinder as he ran alongside the swine.

'They won't go where I want them,' he called, panting after a sow who was just then examining the interior of Ma Bruijntjes' open door.

'I wouldn't let her go in there, if I were you!' exclaimed Baruch as a cry from inside the house announced that the sow was not only in but creating havoc. Jans disappeared after her and emerged, holding his ear, which the matron had boxed, while the pig was shooed back and turned its attention to the garden.

Baruch smiled at the scene but would not allow himself to linger. There was work to be done. It suited him; this quiet, sober life among the villagers, who knew no art or guile. He toiled hard, for there was much to do if he was to eke out a living from lens grinding. But still, he had time to read, to write, to converse by letter with one or two luminaries and, above all, to work it all out. And by "all" he really meant all.

He was at his lathe, trying not to inhale the particles which he could see floating upwards from the pan, when a noise on the steps alerted him.

'Thank you, Karel,' he called, assuming it to be the boy who brought the mail, for today was Wednesday and mail day in the village. But there was no answer, and Baruch halted his leg on the treadmill and looked round.

The door was blocked by a large presence with travelling shawl, an outsized hat, and some baggage under one arm.

The young man squinted, uncertain of who might be there.

'So here's where we'll find you, hidden away like a harvest mouse that makes her home in the hay!' The voice was out of place.

'Moses?' Baruch walked forward, holding a cloth in one hand.

'Does this constitute a roof?' asked the man, glancing up at the thatch, through which large holes were visible, each marked by a corresponding pail on the floor.

'Barely but it serves.'

'Good,' said the man, whose corpulence was aided by

swathes of travelling clothes. 'Because if it was, I would be banned from coming beneath it. What did the curse say? "Nor stay under the roof with him, nor be within four cubits of him". Come here, my boy, and let me embrace you!'

Baruch allowed himself to be engulfed in the rich fabric of the Jewish merchant, breathing in all the scents that his travelling had afforded. Spices and aromatics, food and the road.

'Green Moses!' he said, eventually stepping back, though still holding on to his sleeve.

'Surprised?' asked the traveller, removing his hat and looking round for somewhere to sit.

'And delighted! Here, allow me.' Spinoza scooped up the cat that had wandered in from the village and was just then asleep on the only chair. 'Take your ease, please. And can I get you something? I have milk, or water, or perhaps a little sack?'

'Milk!' said the man, as if taken back 'Milk! Is it kosher?'

Baruch laughed, but not fully. He was not sure if his visitor was joking. 'If you mean have I got it from a Jewish cow, I would have to say no,' he replied without apology. 'There is not much call for kosher around here.'

'I'll take a little water,' said the traveller, warily. Whatever in his conscience had allowed him to visit the exile, did not permit him to break a lifetime of observance in other respects.

He downed the water greedily, thirsty from a fifteen-league walk. 'Now tell me, Baruch Espinoza, how are you and how do you fare?' He looked around, taking in the modest surroundings and the books lining all of one wall. 'You are thriving, or at least surviving?'

Spinoza nodded, drawing up the lathe stool so that he,

too, could sit down. 'I do well, Green Moses. But what of the community? My brother? What of Pedro? What became of him?'

'He had more sense than you!' replied the traveller. 'Recanted and confessed before the anathema was pronounced. He's a good Jew now and so his business thrives. Your brother does well.' He didn't add, "and sends his greetings" and Baruch knew that was because no such greetings had been sent.

'You risk a lot in coming here,' he said, refilling the earthenware bottle from which the visitor had drunk.

'Bah!' spat the man. 'They risked a lot in expelling you. Losing your wisdom and your unorthodox ideas. You could have taught them something, though of course you went too far.'

'I've gone still further of late,' said the young man, beaming with pleasure at seeing his old friend.

'That was always your trouble!' replied the man, putting down the bottle. 'Ever since you were a boy, you went too far. Too far into learning, too far into danger, too far into trouble. I've had it with your "too far!"' he smiled as he spoke, and Baruch knew it was meant kindly.

'But I always had you to rein me in, Green Moses,' he replied, smiling back. 'And I thought I had escaped, but you have found me – even here!'

'Don't worry, I can't stay. I'm on my way to the Leipzig Fair. It's that time of year again. But I set out a week or so early to make a little detour, for I heard you were living somewhere in these parts. Ha! It's good to see you, Espinoza. You haven't changed a bit!'

They fell to discussing the community and how so and so fared, for Baruch had heard of no one since he left

Amsterdam that day. And pretty soon the talk came, as he knew it would, round to the subject for which he'd been cursed.

'And what of all *that*?' said Moses, spreading out his gnarled and ample hands.

'What?'

'*That*!' said the traveller again, as if the word contained all possible meaning.

'Precision was never your speciality,' said Baruch, getting up and walking over to his lathe. 'But I don't think you mean my machinery.'

'No, no!' replied the older man impatiently. 'You know, that. The nonsense, the heresy. The slight on the Torah to which I'd rather not listen, but find myself asking of all the same.'

'Then perhaps you should not.' Baruch was gentle, for he loved the old fellow and appreciated his visit.

'But I have to,' said the old man, looked perplexed. His faith was deep; deep enough to withstand whatever Baruch had to say. He wasn't sure why he asked it.

'Very well. On condition that you stop me if I go "too far" as you put it. I have no wish to hurt you, Green Moses.'

'Pff! A quest for truth never hurt no one!' said the man, using the old Yiddish phrase from his childhood. 'Do your worst, outlawed one.'

'All right. Then has it ever struck you how God appears in scripture? First one thing, then another. To Moses, God is visible – angry and jealous as well. For Micah he sat on a throne, for Ezekiel he was a fire and to Daniel an old man in white. And that's not to mention the God of the Christians who's a Word, a dove and a man!'

Green Moses shrugged. 'So what? The God of our

Fathers is all these things. Barring the Christian business,' he added as an afterthought.

'No, Moses! The God of our Fathers might be. The true God is nothing like this. Don't you see, these are all imaginings? The prophets are men like everyone else, conditioned by the times they lived in, by the message they were keen to impart. And the God they spoke of was their own creation.'

'Then what they say about you is true,' muttered the visitor, shaking his head and looking glum. 'You have lost your faith, after all.'

'Only a faith in stories, in the truth I am convinced.' Baruch drew his stool up closer and put his mind from the work of the day.

'You look to the Torah for truth,' he said, 'And you will find it there. But layered beneath so much that is transient and misleading, that men have mistakenly believed. Do you think,' he added, warming to his theme as the old man took off the fur-lined coat which he deposited on the floor, there being nowhere else to put it, 'for one moment, that God is a person, albeit a very large or wise one? I know that you, as a good Jew, would not. Yet you persist in imagining Him so. The God of the Book, be it Torah or Testament, is a thing most strange. For God does not write books. He does not speak in rules – which food you shall or shan't eat, or which piece of skin you cut off. He does not care because there is no "He" to care. Don't you see that, Green Moses, whose knee I sat at when I was a wondering child?'

The old man shook his head, straining to understand. 'Then there is nothing? No Law to guide our lives?'

'You don't need Law if you heed what is true. And it is this: love God and live a good life. That's the sum of it. All else is constructed by man to subdue or terrify other men. To make them obedient to this or that viewpoint, in short, to frustrate harmony with the Divine and the true expression of themselves, which is one with the Godhead itself.'

'Now you're befuddling me,' Green Moses laughed, though he didn't feel much like laughing for he was longing for something to eat and he found Baruch had not changed. He was as impenetrable and obtuse as before.

'If we are to debate this, I need something to line an empty stomach. Do you not breakfast, or have you done so already?'

'Forgive me, I try not to eat until noon or until I'm hungry,' said Baruch, thinking of the empty stock pot and food larder. 'I can send to Juffrouw Bakker and see if her oven is warm. Maybe she'll have some black bread baked. And we can boil a few things up.'

'Is there a tavern?' asked the visitor abruptly, the last possibility not spiking his appetite. 'Come on, outlawed one! I'll take you there and watch you dine. You look as if you could do with a bit of meat on those heathen bones. Meanwhile I'll stick to something safe. Rabbits don't have to be kosher!'

* * *

The tavern stood apart from the rest of the village of Rijnsburg. It was a squat building, low and mean from without, spacious and warm within. Sand was customarily sprinkled over the flags to dry the mud from men's shoes, but the sand was dry today. Though it was still early in the morning, a goodly number of people were already inside, seated at tables, playing cards and drinking ale from deep stoneware. They were careful, though, not to quaff too quickly or be with too little coin to pay.

The drinkers greeted Benedict warmly, for that was the name by which they knew him, and waved to his companion too. Simple, uncomplicated men; variously toothless but grinning and mostly right-hearted. They didn't distinguish between Jews and Gentiles. Their lives were bounded by the village and the amusements to be found therein. The pattern of the year and their place within it, relations with neighbours and friends, all these made up the essence of both squabbles and joys.

The Jewish Merchant seated himself heavily, groaning a little at his bones. "Sufficient unto the day are the troubles." That trouble could wait till it announced itself more plainly than a little pain in the bones.

'Now what's on offer, heathen?'

He called to the mistress, who brought them some watered down ale which sat on the table between them, while they ordered mutton and potatoes for Spinoza and fat rabbit pie for the guest. The plates arrived, steaming in good rich gravy, and Spinoza felt hungry as the smell wafted up. When he thought about it, he hadn't eaten well in days.

They tucked in, not speaking much, with their napkins around their throats and didn't care that the grease from the table's previous incumbents left marks on their elbows.

Eventually replete, they sat back, wiped their mouths and called for a little more ale.

'I'm afraid my pocket…'

'No, no. This is my note. Allow me to treat you – that's what old men are for. Especially old men who are about to get fat from the offspring of profits. Now, you were just starting to upset me. Are you going to continue?'

Baruch smiled. 'Only if you'll listen and try to comprehend without judging me first.'

'I don't do judgement,' said Green Moses, being something of an outlaw himself, for his name betokened someone who could duck in and out of the community.

'Very well. Then let me ask you. How do you know that God exists?'

Moses paused before replying, the hairs on his chin shaking a little as he considered the question. 'I knows because I know it,' he said finally. '"I am that I am," saith the Lord.'

'You know because you sense it?'

'I knows because I knows it,' he replied again. 'What you getting at, boy?'

'Much as I love you, Green Moses, your faith's on a slippery stone. And plenty of men don't "know it", or at least not in the way you do. So let's firm your ideas and ground them in mathematical reason rather than in the language of man. Imagine a being than which nothing greater can be conceived. Have you got it? Can you picture this greatest conceivable being or get a sense of it? Now, do you agree that it is greater to exist in reality rather than in the mind alone?'

The old man nodded as if he was hanging on for dear life. 'You mean you're greater if you're here than if I simply dreamt you?'

'Exactly! So, given that premise, the greatest conceivable being, if He is to be the greatest, must exist in reality rather than in the mind alone. Therefore the greatest conceivable being must exist and exist necessarily. He cannot not exist, if He is to remain the greatest conceivable being. If He did not then any number of things could surpass Him, things that did exist, such as this table. Therefore God *must* exist. He necessarily exists and cannot be conceived as not existing.'

Moses felt he had somehow been dealt a sleight of hand but could not begin to say why. 'Have you just proved God?' was all he could think to say.

'Much as I'd like to claim it, that argument has been around for years and belongs to a Christian called Anselm. But it's a good one, don't you think? And I'm going to take it further.

'Except God, no substance can be granted or conceived. Or, to put it another way, whatever is, is in God, and nothing can be conceived or exist without God. That's my starting point, Moses, and it's also my end. And you may ask, "What do I mean?" And I will tell you. God is substance, by which I mean a thing whose essence involves existence and whose nature cannot be conceived unless existing. This is hard to grasp, so take it slowly and follow me here. Show me something. Anything!'

'The velvet of my coat, the ale in the beaker, what do you want me to show you?'

'Either of those will do, and neither of them are substances.'

'Feel it!' said the merchant, rubbing his hand on his crimson sleeve. 'It feels like a substance to me.'

'But it doesn't exist by itself. It is the product of something else. Something beyond it caused it to be, whether seamstress or fabric or plant, which before it had a cause and so on. Whereas a substance exists in and of itself. And only one substance exists, namely God. Don't worry, my friend, for everything excellent is as difficult as it is rare.'

The merchant frowned but kept silent.

Baruch continued. 'You want to ask, "what of man? Am

I not a substance, or you?" But do we exist, in and of ourselves, or are we the product of a process beyond us? And can we be conceived of as not existing? Of course we can for, in a while we will both fall asleep and our bodies decay into dust. And the children I have not fathered may, or may not, have existed had things been different for me. You see my point? Man is not substance because man is not essence; we might not exist or we might. Only God is both substance and essence.'

Green Moses was doing his best to understand, but thought that a little more ale might lubricate his mind to work better. He poured it into the beaker and was about to drink when Baruch took it from him and poured almost a quarter of it on the table, to which no harm could be done that it had not already suffered.

'Is the puddle on the table – and now on the floor – ale, Moses?'

'Ay and good drinking stuff too! What did you do that for? You may be clever, but you're often a fool Espinoza!' the old man grumbled, gulping the rest down quickly before it could go the same way.

'So we would say the puddle is in the ale? Careful, it's a nice distinction.'

'The ale is in the puddle?' said the merchant, slightly bleary.

'No, the puddle is in the ale. I'll explain. Could the puddle exist without the ale? No, I've poured it there and it is the ale. It is dependent on the ale for existence. And yet the puddle has actions of its own. It will seep into the table, it will soak into our clothes and it may leave a stain, though I doubt it. But the point is, that the puddle does things that appear independent but are causal because of its nature as ale. It is in ale because it cannot be conceived without the ale that put it there, and yet it does things that the ale wouldn't do, if it had not been poured on the table. And it's like that with God and creation.'

'What are we, the ale or the puddle?'

'I'll say again. Whatever is, is in God, and nothing can be conceived or exist without God. Man, and everything that lives, is a mode of the divine. Nature is a modification or extension of His essence. The puddle if you like. Don't you see? God is not distinct from the world but identical to it. That's why I say nature or God – they are one and the same.'

'Surely, then! This is blasphemy and the elders were right all along? Now you start to hurt me, Baruch, now you start to make me sad. You're saying that God is no more than what I see around me? God is the table, or the ale or the drunk over there in the corner. What nonsense is this?'

Baruch leant back in the chair and wondered if he'd gone too far. It always went this way. People were always upset when their beliefs and their stories were challenged.

'No you're right,' he said, surprisingly, and held up his hands in surrender.

'I'm right?'

'Indeed.'

'And now you're joking with me. I don't know! I come all this way, pay for your food, listen when you speak, don't hit you when you spill my ale and then you mock me and say I'm right when I haven't even put forward my views. How can I be right if all you have said is true?'

'Believe me, you can be,' said the young man, preparing to rise to his feet. 'We can both be right because both of us seek the truth though we express ourselves differently. And both wrong as well, and perhaps far from the mark. But it matters not. What matters is this, that everything's intact. And I mean it, Green Moses, everything's safe and intact. Both you and me and – everything!'

'I don't understand you, boy. Really I don't! You speak in riddles. You're so…' he paused, 'So dense, like the trees in the forest. Take me out of this tavern and I must be on my way or they'll convict me of heresy too, and my business couldn't support it. There's a lot of benefits in being a good Jew, you know, boy. You'd have done well to have heeded that lesson.'

'Maybe,' said Baruch, mildly, kissing his friend on both cheeks. 'Now you look after yourself and listen to those old bones. Do they want to travel to Leipzig?'

'Sure they do. They'll stop complaining when the trading starts. And if they don't, they don't. It's their choice!'

The old man got up and started towards the door and then stopped and turned in his tracks, walked over and sat down with as disgruntled an aspect as could be disguised within a warm heart.

'All right. You can treat me like a fool and humour me because I haven't stomach enough to take it. Or you can press on. And I can force myself to listen and see if there's anything there. And don't ask why I do it, when you're so obviously so stupid a fool! Let's say I do it in memory of your mother who was kind to me when there was no one else. Now, if I order one more flagon are you going to pour that and spill it as well?'

* * *

'I know my thoughts are dense,' said Spinoza, not drinking because it was too early in the day. 'And if I showed you my notebooks you would see they are all based on Euclid and the evidence of geometry, but I will spare you that!'

'Ah, that's more like it. Keep it simple, my boy. Because if it's not simple enough to be readily understood, there's something wrong in the reckoning. You were saying God is the table!'

'Put like that it's absurd. And yet my theory is not absurd but what I genuinely believe to be true. I said that man, and all things, are modes of the Divine; expressions of God if you like. It follows that whatever happens, was always going to happen. Men think themselves free because they are conscious of their own volitions and appetites, and ignorant of the causes of them.'

'Worse than I thought,' said Green Moses. 'Free will is necessary to survive.'

'But I haven't finished yet!' Baruch laughed, because something in the whole situation was absurd and more than the old man had bargained for, and both of them were conscious of it.

'God has infinite attributes, of which we are aware of just two. Thought and Extension. And before you throw up your old hands in horror and find solace for ignorance in drink, you will see that the explanation is easier than it sounds. That beaker, which has served us so well, is two things and may be more. But it is at least two. Firstly it is an idea. You will have a memory of it, or a notion of what a beaker is. The potter who made it conceived it first as Idea. But secondly, it is Extension, or in other words a thing that exists, with atoms that you can hold. Everything is! There is nothing that is neither idea, or thing, or very often both.'

'But why are these "ideas or things" anything to do with God?' Green Moses was beginning to be drawn in.

'Because both ideas and extensions have the character of

something self-sufficient, and as we already know that only God necessarily and truly exists, then both ideas and extensions are aspects of the Divine. They are not separate or distinct which is why everything is sacred.'

'So I should love the beaker of ale as much as I love the Almighty? There's many who would agree with you, but most good Jews would not. And I do not!' he added, putting down the drink. Moses was a man of the world and he knew when he'd had enough, especially with the journey still to come.

'Well this is just it. Perhaps the heart of what I believe. For God does not ask us to love Him, and yet we are required to do so, because we ourselves are not *other* than God. There is only this; the beautiful, eternal Mind that, by existing ceaselessly loves itself. We are part of that Mind, our every action a part of the Divine eternally working itself out; for God is a Mind that thinks. In so far as our minds see things in their eternal aspect, we participate in eternity and are eternal too. That is why I can live my days in such peace.'

'You don't mind that you're banished? That you live your days half starved, with only a cat to know you? Because I would mind that, Baruch! I would mind it, and so I'd change it and get my just desserts.'

'No, I don't mind. When you work with lenses you see things in a different way. Either closer to hand or further away. And it's taught me to see life like that too. *Sub specie aeternitatis*, or under the eye of eternity, through God's eye if you will. Looked at from afar our little problems become very small indeed. Even death seems small, seen under Heaven's eyes.'

'But you don't believe in Heaven,' grumbled the old man, finally being surfeit with discussion.

'Under God all things are possible. Heaven is a word and

words are dangerous things. But what I believe is this; that we are safe, and that all our views have meaning because God has infinite attributes and only one at the same time. Even contradictory views, which seem to rub badly with each other, are somehow necessary and true.'

'That sounds like having your cake and eating it,' said the old man, starting to gather his things together. 'What I said before about keeping things simple had some truth in it you know, heathen. I'll stick with my faith and you stick with yours, and we'll go our separate ways. I'll think kindly of you though, child, for you have a fearsome mind. I'll give you that. Your mother would have been proud of you, had you been a bit more Jewish, you know!'

'Being Jewish was a struggle. Being Christian, I'm sure, would also be,' said Baruch, rising to his feet as well. 'Too much to take on trust, too many stories around. But, if they accord with you, then that is also good. One thing I know, Green Moses, and I'm sounding the more senior now, the more you struggle to live the less you live. Give up the notion that you must be sure of what you're doing. Instead, surrender to what is real within you, for that alone is sure. You are above everything distressing.'

'I wonder, child! I wonder! Maybe I'll think of your words when I'm old and ill and these bones, that are already grumbling, start to sing out a bit more. Then perhaps I'll think of this talk. But until then, I have trading to do.'

'Then go your way, Green Moses, and peace be on you,' cried Baruch, jumping up, suddenly keen to be back at his lathe. 'And thank you,' he added.

They parted company, properly this time. Green Moses went one way and Baruch Spinoza back to his seat by the window. Moses had not gone more than two miles down the road when a pretty sight assailed him; a clump of primroses growing in the lee of an elder tree. He stopped to examine them and saw another just feet away, and then cowslips and bluebells as well. And as he looked, a bee alighted, moving her antennae excitedly, for the pollen was still untouched and she was the first to find it.

'Is that you, Lord?' Green Moses muttered under his breath. And, absurd as it sounded, he suddenly understood that everything *was* a mystery, more profoundly than he had thought before. And if he, Green Moses, did have God living in him, was an "aspect of God", that was how Baruch had put it, life took on a very different meaning.

It was sanctified. It was safe. It had meaning. And there was no trouble there at all.

* * * * * * * *

The journalist and the philosopher were back on the mountain, the book lay quiet between them and the Sage Train had swung back into view.

'It's because we're nearer, we're going up,' whispered Chesterton, anxious not to be seen. 'They might not like us spying on them,' he added, to which Nietzsche assented vigorously. '*Nein, nein*. Please, let us not annoy them. And please will you hide that book!'

They settled themselves behind a gorse bush, pushed so close together as to be almost touching; their hats just visible to the discerning eye. It was Nietzsche who had grabbed the book and now held it sandwiched between them.

'I think we're well hidden,' said Chesterton, manoeuvring his enormous frame.

'You're sticking out!' hissed Nietzsche. 'Your leg! It's sticking out!'

'Thank you!' said the journalist gruffly, heaving the offending limb with both hands. He glowered at the philosopher and, finding him crouching so low that he would scarcely be visible to a rabbit, decided that they were safe enough for the time being. The book appeared unperturbed.

'I love Spinoza,' Chesterton whispered, as the man himself was not twenty feet away, his young face radiant. 'I think he is the noblest of all believers. Not afraid to follow his God when he found a definition which was big enough not to limit Him.'

'But he was hardly a theist,' hissed Nietzsche. 'More a

pantheist – finding God all around. And in the most surprising places. He's not your typical theist.'

'Who wants a typical theist? And you can't say that Baruch was fearful! He's not quite right for everyone. For me, orthodoxy is the best vehicle. I just jump on board and go. But for souls that need to search a little, Spinoza's a good place to start.'

Nietzsche was more quiet than normal. Chesterton didn't know whether it was fear of being discovered or something else that was disturbing him. He was certainly less cocksure.

'I would so like to,' he said eventually.

'So like to what?'

'Believe in a God. But I find that I cannot, however much I try. Of course, being an atheist allowed me to construct my own philosophy, but in the depths of my heart I would like to find out what it is you all see.'

Chesterton was silent at that. It had never occurred to him that beneath all the arrogance and bluster lay a soul as timid as the rest of them.

'Will you excuse me,' said the philosopher in the same humble vein, 'if I slip out for a little? There is something I just have to do. And will you hold this – keep it safe,' he added.

'Yes, yes. Call of nature. I understand,' said Chesterton bluffly. But the philosopher was already gone, crawling on his stomach like a man on a battlefield and glancing nervously over his shoulder lest the Sages should see him.

When he had gone a little way down the mountain, and was sure he was well out of sight, he jumped up and flew to a scene.

'There might not be a God,' he mused, as he swept up looking for someone to help, 'But while I have it in my power... power is a thing of our making.'

He found them quickly; a boy in a war, who had been hit by canon and had fallen from his wounded mount. The horse was still alive and the boy's legs lay trapped beneath her.

Acting swiftly, and with the utmost compassion, the philosopher closed the mare's eyes. He sent her back to the field she had grazed in when she was a foal. Then, turning his attention to the boy, grasped him firmly round the thighs and pulled with all of his strength. This did nothing, for Nietzsche was not very strong. But, sensing perhaps a new will, the boy shifted and tried to move.

'That's right,' breathed the philosopher. 'Now, on the count of three. One, two, three!' There was a terrific struggle and the boy's legs were suddenly free. 'There may not be a God, but there is me,' said Nietzsche to himself, skulking back up the mountain to resume his place in the gorse. In the distance, medical orderlies were placing the lad on a stretcher. He had been given a chance, it seemed, and the philosopher could hear them speaking.

'You're the lucky one, mate. How did you get clear of her? You've got some luck on your side!'

'If I can spend at least some of these days doing good to others! Then I am the richer for helping!' He looked about him. The valley was overtaken with scenes layered one upon the other, in a tapestry of lives, with their attendant disasters and joys. But none of the people down in the valley could see beyond their own scene. Just like the boy, they were trapped there, wrapped up in their own small lives. Only the philosophers could see things as they were. And it seemed that one joy was not so dissimilar to another, and one pain not so far from the rest.

'Better?' said Chesterton conspiratorially.

'Better!' said the philosopher.

'Well, we've only time for one more. For the Sages are nearly upon us. What say you if we go back to the beginning? Because, if I remember, we dealt with the Ancients most poorly – only that thoughtless Aristippus.'

'Not Plato or Socrates, for we will never agree on their precedence!' They both peered at the tattered volume that was now lying quite inert, as if waiting for their decision.

'No, no, I was thinking of neither,' sighed Chesterton. 'Though they equally have a good claim. No, I was thinking of the other great heathen who has shaped our world so profoundly. I'm proposing we read about Aristotle.'

'Remember the rules of the book. Wherever possible we don't visit directly but see through another man's eyes. That's been slipping of late. I'm quite sure they've twisted their tales.' Nietzsche had a bit of mud down one side of his face. It made him look more human. 'And as it's the last,' he continued. 'Let us hope it is modern.'

'Very well. And by great good chance I find that Aristotle *is* up to date. The prevailing ethic of the day, although few would label it so. But, in their decisions most people do try to be good. Now, I know you don't like virtue, Herr Professor but please, as it's the last, just let it go.'

'I never said I didn't like virtue! In fact the opposite is true. To Aristotle then, and perhaps some common ground?'

'To Aristotle,' said Chesterton, and thumped the German good-naturedly on the back. They flipped the pages of the book back to near the beginning, that was also, curiously, the end.

* * * * * * * *

The British Library, London.
October 2015

Aristotle

'Sorry, Sir, we're closing in ten minutes. Will you require it tomorrow?'

David sighed, rubbed his eyes and knocked off his glasses. They fell on the manuscript and he couldn't pick them up. So he couldn't see. Only the dim blur of the parchment and the ancient text before him. The beautiful Greek, obscured.

'Yes – please,' he spoke slowly, with effort. 'If I haven't bruised it! Could you – just – put those on for me?'

'Certainly, Sir. I'll take my gloves off first. Your glasses are a bit less precious, you see!' The attendant removed his white cotton gloves, picked up the glasses and repositioned them, carefully, on David's head.

'Aagh! Thank you. That's better! Now at least I can say goodnight to her.'

'Is it interesting, Sir? I've seen you in here all week. What is it you're studying, if you don't mind me asking?'

Outside, the dark London night fell hard against the windows.

'A Greek text. Very old. One of the very few fragments by a female we have…' he paused to glance up at the woman who had come to push the wheelchair.

'Anna. I hope I haven't kept you.' The woman bent down

solicitously, easing his arms into a coat to protect him from the cold outside. She clicked the lock off the wheels and manoeuvred it towards the doors.

'Goodnight,' the man called to the attendant who was placing the precious leaves into a sealable Perspex tray.

'Goodnight, Sir. See you tomorrow.' As he locked up and turned out the lights, he reflected on this very brave man who came to the library every day, and never once seemed to think himself worse off than anyone else. 'It's a pity there aren't more like him in the world,' he told his wife that night over a meal from the Tesco 'finest' range. His wife merely grunted. She was watching the telly.

* * *

Stageira, Ancient Greece c 340 BC

"Today we watched the starlings fly. They moved as a body with the hawk above, a group to hide the young. Aristos said it was like the city with the polis protecting us all.

From dawn to dusk I roam. The great god Hermes slips through our window carrying the sunbeam in his arms. I rise from the bed, where I sleep with my mother. The porter is roused.

'Go back to sleep, fat Xerxes' I say (to him).

For fifteen summers long, I am favoured by the gods. My body is swift as a boy's. My master says that I am as good as a boy. He has taught me how to write.

My master writes words and invents them — logic, purpose, reason, physics — for "without words how might ideas be explored?" Students wait to attend him, for he tutored the emperor himself, but I am not a student.

Together, we study the fish in the pond.

'What is their purpose, Master?'

'To be the best fish they can possibly be,' he says. 'Fish fulfilled in their being.'

Oft times my master leaves us. He travels abroad for knowledge. Then, slaves go (with him). They harness the ox carts to go to the great beyond. He talks of (the) virtue(s) and tells me to name them. I sit in the sunlight to do so.

Wisdom is the first; Phronesis and Sophia. Sophia is female like me while Phronesis is masculine wisdom; what is learnt or known by practice. Sophia's comes by instinct. But wisdom in both their incarnations is the first of my master's virtues."

* * *

When it came to it, David didn't return to the British Library the next day. Anna was sick, so it was an agency carer who arrived in the morning to dress him. Jake was slow and too careful, so he missed his taxi slot, and by the time they had found another with wheelchair access, it was past twelve o'clock and most of the day was gone. So he sat alone in the flat, watching his computer and listening to the screams of the tube trains as they hurtled towards Shepherd's Bush Market.

Anyone else would have been got down by it; the injustice of the creeping illness that worked its way up his limbs. And on certain days he was low. Days when his hands were so useless he couldn't type, or so leaden he couldn't turn the pages of his books. But if his body was slowing, his mind still danced. He had a family who loved him and above all he had his work. The double first from Oxford had stood him in good stead; given him something to fall back on when he could no longer hold down a job. Money was more of a problem because there was no income at all beyond the government handouts, but who needs money when you have a mind?

The phone went at six. He managed to answer it and put it on speaker because it was the end of the day and he hadn't the strength to hold the receiver. He knew who it would be.

'Hello, Dad. Is that you?'

'David! How are you, lad? Have you had a good day?' His father's ebullient cheerfulness flowed down the receiver with octogenarian health.

'Not bad, Dad, though there was a cock-up with getting to the library.'

'Bugger them. Too slow at dressing you again? I'd come round there and do it myself if I could. But they won't let me out, lad. Some God-awful number pad on the door to keep the loonies in. I'm planning an escape though. They didn't call me "Digger Paul" for nothing you know!'

'I know, Dad, though Foxglove Nursing Home might be a bit more secure than Colditz, and I have to remind you that you didn't actually ever escape – even from the Germans.'

'Not for the want of trying, my lad. Anyway, glad you're alright. And I mean it. I'll be round in the morning.'

'Whatever you say, Father. Got to go. The new carer doesn't know how to get in and I'll have to shout the key safe number through the bloody keyhole or else she'll batter the door down.' The whirr of the wheelchair woke the cat, as he sped past on his way to the door.

'Three, six, six, nine.'

'Three, six, six, five?'

'No, three, six, six, nine – nine.'

'Three, double six, double nine?'

'No! Three, six, six, nine!' She managed to let herself in eventually and, during the time it took to heat up the macaroni cheese and feed him, he learned all about her. She was a happy satanist who revered Aleister Crowley and regularly performed the black mass on her living room floor.

'Is that why you have a pentacle dangling from your lower lip?' he asked mildly.

She looked at him as if he were mad. 'No, luv. That's just for beauty. My boyfriend's got one through 'is knob!' When she washed him later, David felt he could only be a disappointment, being so spectacularly unadorned.

True to his word, his father did arrive the next day just as Anna, snuffling and streaming with cold, was heating up some porridge. David's surprise was only half invented.

'Well, bugger me! How the hell did you get out?'

'I've tamed one!' His father tapped his nose. 'Can't be long though.' He winked in the lovely conspiratorial way he had. It was the wink he had used for as long as David could remember which basically meant "everything's fine". 'She's risking life and limb in giving me the combination. I'll have to be back before she goes off shift because that's when there'll be a rout. There'll be a bloody head count!'

His father's occupation of the nursing home had been something of a surprise for everyone. He had come to the decision himself; sold the house and signed all the documents quite cheerfully, saying he was a "bloody old worry to everyone and better off out of the way", but from the moment he had arrived in the clean little room he had set about escaping. Never was he in better spirits than when he had slipped away to stalk a Nazi on Ealing Broadway, or hop on a tube in a bid for friendly Golders Green. The staff had been worried at first, and most of the junior officers at the local police station had spent several hours looking for him at one time or another. But, over the years, the Foxglove staff realised that he always turned up in time for tea, and it kept him more amused than Scrabble, so they'd learned to turn a blind eye.

David was not so amused. 'Look, Dad,' he said between gulps, as Anna ladled the porridge into his mouth. 'You've, got to stop escaping. There's nothing to escape from!'

His father narrowed his eyes, picked up an imaginary rifle and aimed it at the cat, which ignored him. 'There's a Hun round every corner, lad! What you talking about? Of course there's something to escape from!'

David gave up. 'All right, Dad. If you say so. You'd better have a cup of tea. Got a letter from Jason today.' He tried to pick up the airmail but his fingers were blunt, so Anna did it for him.

His father sat down abruptly. 'Who's Jason?' he said, with just a touch of malevolence.

'Jason. Your son. My brother!'

'The one who avoided conscription?'

'The one who is a successful banker and lives in New York with his very pretty girlfriend, and who phones you from time to time, when you pretend not to know him.'

'As I said, the one who avoided the call-up.' David looked at him. Sometimes he wondered whether his father's habitual lunacy had more meaning than he let on.

'Anyway, how are you, my brave soldier? How's the gangrene?' his father continued.

David laughed. 'I haven't got gangrene, you silly old

codger,' he said, as he swallowed a handful of vitamins. 'I've got bloody MS as you very well know.'

'Multiple shrapnel wounds? Yes, yes, I remember. What a damned shame.'

'Something like that,' said David, giving up again. There was simplicity in this madness. 'Do you want a ride in the taxi?'

'Yes, you can drop me at Dunkirk,' replied his father, buttering himself a fat bread sandwich. 'Should make it onto one of the little boats, then back to the glittering cliffs.'

As they pulled away from Foxglove, and Paul allowed himself to be led through the gates by the attractive young nurse, David reflected that wisdom took many forms. His father's was another variety, but it was wisdom enough in its way. A combination of practical and intuitive – at any rate it got him through the days.

Anna left him by the reading desk. He ordered Deposit 3917 from the Rare Manuscript Department and waited quarter of an hour while they retrieved it. He found that his mouth was quite dry with excitement by the time the trolley stopped beside him, and the attendant handed him the parchment sheets which he spread out like a deck of cards because David hadn't the dexterity to handle them. David savoured the moment before he started work. It was here all before him, waiting to be uncovered beneath the cold, unknown symbols. When he closed his eyes he could imagine her; this lithe, unnamed girl, dancing her way across the landscape of Ancient Greece.

He could imagine her, and he was a little in love with her. He was in love with the sunlight of her existence and the respect she had for her master. But more than anything, he was in love with the thought that this was very possibly an original scribe of Aristotle, who had so long eluded the scholars. Overlooked, until now, because no one had thought it possible, given his views on women. But the Greek was clear, and the more he read, the more David was convinced. There was just no one else it could be referring to. And what an insight into the man! It brought him to life. Not stiff or remote, but lively, simple, unadorned. The only tragedy lay in all that was lost. The six pages they had were of stiffened parchment, so thin in places that each yellowed strand was visible and the oak-gall ink so faded, that whole sections were suddenly lost.

It seemed to be a discussion of what made a virtuous man; Aristotle's famous "golden mean", whereby all noble qualities were sandwiched between the vices of deficiency and excess. So, the virtue of courage was the middle path between the vice of cowardliness (too little of it) and foolhardiness (too much). Aristotle had often been accused of being a middle-aged kind of thinker, but here in the immediacy of the text he seemed a ghostly, vibrant mind. David blinked several times to adjust his eyes, bent forward to position himself and started to read. He translated as he went, aware that his own rendering was a clumsy defilement of the original arching Greek.

* * *

"Today we studied the embryo. In the egg, the chick was forming, its sac of yolk attached by a cord, down which the atoms flow.'

The master's teacher was Plato, who taught of the perfect Form; the unseen source from which all else flows. My master scoffs at this. He says we should not look for phantoms when everything is laid out to see. His is a world of experience whilst Plato's is the world of ideals."

The text broke off there, infuriatingly, for there was a tear down one side of the parchment with just the last words preserved and these were damaged. He saw the word ψρόυησις again, meaning wisdom, and the symbols for *eudaimonia* which, for the Greeks, meant the greatest kind of happiness attainable. He pored over the text, furious with the loss which tore the girl away. Furious, also, with his eyes which were getting tired and refusing to focus properly. But there it was, laid out for all to see. Damn his bloody fingers that lay clawed in his lap, making it impossible to do internet research. Damn the bloody fool who had torn the parchment at some stage in its long history. Damn the creeping hands of the library clock that suggested that hours had passed while he deciphered the text, and that at any moment Anna would push her head round the door. And now it was Friday and he would have to wait till Monday to resume. Damn it all! He returned to the Greek for a few last, precious moments.

> "Happiness…. derived from living well. There is no such thing as a good act, only a good man and he alone is happy. My master says it is virtue we must strive for. Wisdom, Justice, Courage and Judgement. A man who practices these; he alone is content."

* * *

'Shall we get a pizza?' Her thin coat was no protection. She was hungry, she was cold and she couldn't quite face doing battle with David's archaic cooker, and in any case there was probably no food in the house.

'Can I afford one?'

'Not really, but your carer's allowance came in today, and I suggest you spend it on me!'

The door on the fast-food joint opened outwards, and it was impossible to pull it open and get the wheelchair through at the same time without the door swinging back and hitting him. David winced as they did so, but laughed it off, saying his legs didn't feel anything anyway.

They ordered a twelve inch pepperoni with garlic mushrooms and a glass of house red each. 'Dining in style,' said Anna with an undercurrent of bitterness which David chose to ignore. She sat on his right so she could bend round to offer the glass to his lips. All the same, it was hard not to spill it while sitting down, so she had to stand up to pour it.

'Shall we ask for a straw?' he said finally. 'Then you don't have to jump up.' Speech was difficult for him when he was tired, so she did most of the talking.

'The children are fine,' she said, conversationally, picking off a jalapeno, which looked like it might kill him. 'I spoke to them all today. James is doing a sky dive on Saturday.'

David nodded, concentrating on not choking.

'Could you just…'

Anna looked disgruntled. She had been feeding him for ten minutes and her own food was getting cold.

'Could I just what?'

'Could you just pull my foot to the left? It's fallen off.'

She bent down under the tablecloth, aware that her jumper had ridden up and the top of her buttocks were bare.

'No it hasn't! It's still on the footrest.'

'It feels like it's fallen off.'

'Well it's just a feeling,' she said, pulling the dead weight of the leg a bit. She loaded his fork and posted a section of gooey cheese into his mouth before finally turning her attention to her own plate.

'Could you just…'

'For Christ's sake!'

'I need water. It's too strong.'

She got up and went in search of a waiter, but they were all busy so, eventually, she found a discarded jug on another table and poured the stale water into his wine glass.

'There?'

'Better!'

'Can I eat mine now – please?'

He nodded, his mind in Athens.

Anna chewed for a few minutes, half wondering if she could ask for the plate to be heated up. But there was still no waiter and she was starting to want to go home.

'What do you think of virtue?' he asked, slowly.

'Over-rated.'

'How so?'

'Well, whoever heard of anyone being virtuous and having fun? It's so middle aged. Middle of the road. I think it's better to be radical and dare to be different. Luigi says hello.'

David grunted. He didn't want to be reminded of Luigi.

'We're going to Venice next weekend. I've phoned the agency and warned them. They say it will probably be the new guy, Jake, again.'

David grunted again. The twin prods of that bit of news were each sharp in their own way but, on balance, he minded more about the inadequacies of Jake than his wife going off with her lover.

'Do you mind?' she asked, wanting some reaction.

'Yes, he's an imbecile.'

'Which one?'

'Both!' They smiled at each other amiably. She never loved him more than when he exhibited the extraordinary generosity that allowed her not to suffer his fate.

'Because if you do mind, I won't go. You know that, don't you? You come first.'

'I know. Could you just give me a bit of tomato?'

'Why won't you talk to me? Why do you refuse to enter into anything remotely important? Anything about us?'

'Don't start, Anna.'

'I'm not starting. But this is impossible. I want to talk to you – I mean really talk. Have a dialogue. Find out what you're thinking and whether the presence of Luigi hurts you. And all you do is shut down. Float away on some airy, intellectual cloud and leave me guessing. I mean for Christ's sake. I'm flesh and blood sitting here. Still your wife. You have a duty to let me in!'

David sighed, tried to reach out for her, but knocked the wine glass over. Pink water cascaded over them both as the glass splintered loudly on the floor.

Anna jumped up, mopping distractedly. 'Idiot!'

'No, you're the idiot.'

She laughed, suddenly happy and he laughed too. 'Both idiots then. Shall we go home?'

She pushed him out of the door, thinking that he was one in a million even though he was a bloody nuisance at times. His flat was tiny and unprepossessing, having about it the staleness of stasis. When they had shared a family home it had been more of a joyous place. But then the illness gripped, and he lost his job and eventually the house. So now they both lived in run-down apartments divided by just a few streets. They had never divorced. Anna said she couldn't see how total paralysis could possibly be an adequate cause.

Later that night, when she had washed him and hauled his legs into bed, he looked at the patch of damp above his head and said, 'Isn't it strange that for many of us life is actually less comfortable than it was two thousand years ago.'

'You don't mean that,' she said, giving him a Temazepam to help him sleep. 'What about toothache and running water and hot baths and aeroplanes?'

'Three out of four they had, and the last just spoils the environment. No. Think about it. For the Ancient Greeks, life was a civilised affair. They existed in a world of order with the leisure to organise beauty around them. Their days were spent in discussion and enquiry. No daily battle with mould growing round the taps and a cistern that leaks and drips.'

'You just have to pay someone to mend it! Anyway, their beauty was built on slavery. I'm sure everyone would have the time to do all sorts of wonderful things if they didn't go out to work or toil away at home. No society is civilised if it employs another to do its dirty work.'

'Aristotle would disagree.'

'Aristotle lived a long time ago.' She pulled the duvet under his chin, set the timer on the television and prepared to leave.

'Aristotle thought some are born slaves and only the philosopher's is the life worth living.'

'Then he should have got his hands more dirty. I'm on call at the shelter tomorrow, so I won't be able to come again till Tuesday. Good luck with Jake.'

'Goodnight. And thank you,' he breathed, though it was really an effort now.

'Goodnight.' She closed the door and left him alone. He had his lifeline that he could press if he needed to. Sometimes, she felt, he actually preferred it that way. Dancing through the fields of Arcadia, when he could hardly turn over in bed.

* * *

Saturday mornings always loomed big. He felt he was sitting – not standing – at the bottom of the weekend with a whole balloon of time to fill before Monday. Anna was at the homeless shelter dealing with the after-effects of ethanol on empty stomachs, so he was left to the ministrations of whichever carer the agency sent. Today it was Rosie.

'Can you order me a taxi?' he said, as soon as she had let herself in.

She looked at him in exasperation. 'Well, yes, if that's what you want. But I thought I might dress you first!'

'Obviously. But we need to order it now, to get one with wheelchair access. Can you just do it please?' Rosie was forty and simple. She trotted off and made a great deal of fuss ringing round the cab companies. Anna would have known which one to try. Eventually the taxi was ordered for eleven, and David was dressed, fed, shaved and toileted. He was so used to it that he no longer felt any embarrassment when strangers did the most intimate things. His body lived a long way down from his mind.

The taxi driver helped him out but he was on his own when he got to Foxglove. There was a short and furious battle with an intercom that was placed too high on the wall, but eventually he was in, surrounded by the paradoxical smell of perfumed pee. 'Your father's still in bed,' said Angelique with a hint of apology. She was missing her own father in Antigua. 'Says he's too tired for today.'

'That's not like him,' said David, manoeuvring his wheelchair into the lift. His father's room was on the second floor as an added deterrent to flight.

Paul was sitting up in bed, propped against the pillows and looking out through the window as the first specks of snow floated down. His face brightened immediately when he saw his son.

'What ho, lad! Didn't expect to see you in Colditz. How d'you get in?'

'They let me in,' said David, as he positioned the wheelchair as close to the bed as he could, barging the commode out of the way. 'How are you, Dad? Why aren't you up yet? Haven't the wardens been in?'

'I'm dying,' said his father, in a matter of fact way.

'You're not!' He tried to reach over to clasp the gnarled old hand resting on the bedspread, but he couldn't do it. 'What do you mean you're dying? You look all right to me.'

'No, I mean it, son. I'm dying. Three, six, six, five.'

'Sorry?'

'Three, six, six, five. The year I lost my virginity and the year you were born. Also the pin to the Barclays account.'

'Also the number to my front door. Isn't that odd?'

'Not really, son. Life is full of threads we don't see.'

They sat and looked at each other, while outside the snowflakes thickened. 'You're a good lad,' said Paul finally, leaning forward so that he could touch David's hand. 'Always have been – a good soldier. And so is that wife of yours.'

David shifted uncomfortably. 'I try. But you're a great Dad.'

Paul leant back into the pillows. 'It was easy,' he said,

fiddling with his pyjama buttons. 'But what's the point of malingering here? Help me get up, son, and we'll see what sport we can have with the guards.'

The only help David could offer was encouragement, when the soup-stained jumper looked like it was trying to be put on back to front, and when the slippers slipped away to hide slyly under the bed. It took Paul an hour to dress himself, so by the time the two of them were on their way to the café down the street it was nearly three o'clock. But neither of them minded that much. They sat in the warm conviviality of shared experience, sweet tea and steamed up windows, besides which the filter of Paul's insanity was neither here nor there.

'What's the secret then, Dad?' said David, struggling to manhandle a teacake.

'Bash 'em. Never give up,' replied his father, having won the battle with his own.

'Just the Germans or anyone else?' His father pondered the question. 'Well, the Blackshirts too, of course. Mussolini's lot are pretty nasty. But no, that's about it. Oh, and always stick together. And finally,' his father paused for maximum effect. 'Look after your eyes!'

David laughed. 'Why the eyes in particular? Or are you going to tell me that they're the window to the soul?'

His father looked perplexed. 'No,' he said finally, having thought about the question for some time. 'They're what you see with.' He paused again. 'And if you can't see, then you don't know what's coming next.'

'Does it really matter what's coming next? Sometimes I think it's better not to know. With this bloody illness I don't really want to see what's coming next!'

His father looked concerned. 'No,' he said. 'No, I can

see that. But, if I didn't have my eyes I couldn't even do that. So, I'm afraid I'm right, lad. Look after your eyes.' They ordered another cup of tea and watched the young mothers do battle with pushchairs and shopping bags, and silence fell between them.

'How's your brother?'

David manoeuvred his tea mug onto the edge of the table, hoping it would stay there. 'He's fine, Dad, thank you,' he said in amazement. His father never initiated the topic of Jason.

'He didn't fight in the war.' His father began his usual, unswerving litany.

'No, I know, Dad. But neither did I, and maybe he fights his own battles.'

'I doubt it,' said his father grumpily. He looked up. 'I don't remember why, but I don't want him to get it, lad. I mean it. I don't want him to get it.'

'Get what?' This was a new departure.

'The loot. The bounty. Call it what you will.'

'What are you talking about, Father? Are we on a pirate ship now?'

'No, we're in Colditz,' his father snapped instantly. 'Or we were – till a few moments ago.'

'Right, yes. But there's no loot in Colditz, is there?'

'Plenty of it, lad, you'll see. Plenty of it. But I don't want him to get it. Better hush up though,' his father tapped his nose and looked round suspiciously. 'Walls have ears, my lad, walls have ears.'

'No they don't, Father. God, you're a silly old fool. Half the time I don't know what you're going on about!'

'Just as well, lad. Half the time I don't either! Now, has that wheelchair of yours got any juice in it? Can't miss the afternoon roll call you know. They feed you after that!'

'But you've just had two mugs of tea and a teacake.'

'Have I?' his father looked distracted. 'Well I never! Still, never mind. Best to be back. It keeps 'em busy when they know you're inside. You're a good lad, David. A brave, fighting man. Always have been. And so is that wife of yours!'

The phone went at six o'clock on Sunday morning. The girl at the nursing home said that she was very sorry to have to tell him, but Paul had died in the night. It seems he had suffered a heart attack though there was no sign of any distress, and it could almost appear that he had died in his sleep, were it not that he was found stretched out on the floor. He was beside the open window. She thought he might have been looking at the snow.

David sat, with the phone line dangling beside the bed, until the "off the hook" sound forced him to fish it back up and grapple it to the machine. With a huge effort he compelled himself to swing round, till he could sit on the edge of the bed. Then he raised his right hand in salute. And then he gave in to the tumultuous, convulsing sobs.

* * *

Jason, admittedly, did look obscenely well when he met him at the airport that evening. His battles were more of the skirmish variety than all-out bloodshed and, as he invariably won, his wounds, at least to the naked eye, were negligible. Masked as they were by money, sharp suits and aftershave so expensive it turned most female heads, he breezed through life with the sort of airy assurance that David could only envy.

'I'm sorry,' he said, striding over to the wheelchair. 'I came as soon as I could. The first flight as soon as you'd phoned.'

'Yes, thank you. He would have been sorry he missed you.'

Jason looked discomforted. 'I doubt that, somehow. But I am sorry I missed him. Really sorry. When did you see him last?'

'Yesterday,' replied David, manoeuvring the control button so he could speed up alongside his brother. 'I saw him yesterday. We had tea together. He was in good form actually. Cheerful and robust – you know, his usual self.'

'I can imagine! Don't suppose he mentioned me?'

'He did actually.' David smiled. Just being in the company of his patently successful brother always lifted his spirits. 'He said that he often thought of you and hoped you were OK and that he would very much like to show you the bunker he'd dug out in his room, the next time you were on the front line.'

'Wow!' Jason had stopped in his tracks peering down at his brother in disbelief 'Did he really? I thought he would have said I was a n'er do well who didn't fight in the bloody war.'

'He changed his mind at the last,' his brother lied. 'Said you were a bloody good fighting man – in your own way.'

They made their way to the nursing home where Angelique showed them up. 'De undertakers came an took your fader's body this afternoon,' she said, in a slightly awed voice. Death always took her that way. 'We have cleaned his room and organised 'is things. I expect you'd like a little time alone. Can I get you a nice cup of tea dere? Or coffee? A milky coffee?'

'Don't suppose you have a macchiato?' said Jason with a winning smile.

'Christ!' said David, 'We're not in your Café Grumpy now!'

To the surprise of them both, Angelique got the

reference. 'I've bin there you know. Bin to Café Grumpy. I hears they're bringin dem here to London. We'll just be able to pop out and get one oder de road soon!'

The weak "instant" she brought in stained china cups was not quite the same thing.

'Well, at least it's not one of those awful plastic beakers with a lid and somewhere to suck,' said Jason, as he held his at arm's length, looking like it might be infected.

'No, but actually it might be easier,' his brother replied.

'Oh gosh, sorry. Do you want me to hold it for you?'

'No, just get Angelique back and ask her to put it in a mug and give me a straw, would you?' His brother complied, his whole presence filling the corridor as he sought out the nurse.

'So this was where he spent his days. Dad I mean,' he said, returning, triumphant, with a straw. 'I've often tried to imagine what his room would be like. Do you think he was happy here?'

'I'm not sure happiness came into it,' said David, lowering his head to suck. 'He was content. He had the great art of contentment, born I think, of knowing he'd done his best.'

'In the war?'

'In the war, but also in life. He always gave one hundred percent. Always pushed himself and taught us to do the same, don't you think?'

'Yes, I suppose you're right. He was a great improviser, wasn't he? Do you remember how he would tinker with the Atco until he got it going? Every Sunday. Must have driven Mum to distraction.'

'Yes, but by the end of the day, the bloody lawn would always be mown!' They laughed. The fact of their very different lives made no difference whatsoever to the friendship that had connected them since childhood.

'I don't think he'd mind that much,' said David. 'Dying I

mean. Not after Mum went. Think the light flickered a bit for him then. He was never quite the same after that.'

'Maybe they'll be together again now. United in a blissful afterlife. Peeling the potatoes for a celestial Sunday lunch!'

'Christ, I hope not. That would mean he'd still be battling with the Atco!'

'Well, maybe it will be fixed in Heaven! Maybe there's a heavenly engineer just waiting to mend every clapped-out, recalcitrant machine!'

'Then let's hope the same bloke can do something for clapped-out, recalcitrant bodies.'

The laugh on Jason's lips faded immediately. 'Yeah. How are you, bro? I mean really. How are you?'

'Buggered!' said David, taking a long suck of the fawn liquid. 'Absolutely stuck.'

'I'm sorry,' said his brother, putting his hand on David's arm and squeezing it hard. 'I'm really, really sorry.'

The man in the wheelchair looked up. 'Yeah well,' he said finally, 'Can't be helped. There's no use moaning about it, is there? And I have my work. Did I tell you about the Greek girl, the slave of Aristotle?'

'No, but I've a feeling you're going to!'

'Not now. I'll tell you when we've got Dad a bit more sorted out. What's in that awful black bag?'

Jason rummaged around pulling out a selection of crumpled things. Old man's clothes, along with his glasses' case, some books, a thin blue box containing his Distinguished Service Medal, and a long envelope with the words "Last Will and Testament" inscribed in a shaky hand.

They looked at each other. 'Shall we open it?' said Jason finally. 'There won't be much, surely? I mean he didn't get much for the house and this place soaked up the rest. He's been in here a few years now. Don't suppose our poor old Dad had anything much to leave.'

'I don't know,' said David, his mind returning uncomfortably to his father's last conversation. 'Look. Maybe we can leave this to later. It's a bit unseemly to be poring over the Will before we've even cremated him. Don't you think?'

'Not really,' said Jason, picking up the letter and fingering it. 'I think he would want us to know.'

'I really disagree,' said his brother, trying to grab the envelope. 'Don't, Jason. There's no need. Not now.' But it was too late. Jason had slit open the envelope and brought out a single piece of lined paper. David watched his face as he read it.

'My last Will and Testament. It's very short. Not more than a few lines and dated... dated yesterday!' He was silent as he scanned it and then said ' Well!... There we go!' and put down the sheet, his face instantly pale.

'What did it say?'

'He's left the whole lot to you. One thousand pounds to Anna and a thousand to each of your kids. And then all the rest to you. I'm not mentioned at all.'

He got up and went to stand by the window, pushing the hair back out of his eyes. He looked drained and tired, suddenly older than his thirty-three years. His back hunched forward round the shoulders as if the world had just fallen through his arms, and he had somehow failed to catch it.

'I thought you said he'd talked of me – yesterday?' David could hear his brother's voice hardening as he battled with the shock. 'It's not the money. Of course it's not the money. I couldn't care less about that. It's knowing that, for some reason, Dad thought so little of me that he chose to ignore me completely. Cut me out as they say. And for what? What the hell have I done to be so… unloved?'

David was silent. Eventually he said, 'I don't think it was anything you'd done. I think it was because you buggered off to America and I was struck down by this bloody illness, and in Dad's brain everything became muddled, and you were somehow to blame. It's not that he didn't love you. He just got really, really confused – at the end, I mean.'

'Some confusion!' Jason's voice was tight with hurt.

'He didn't mean it, you know.' David whirred his way over to the window to be beside him. 'If you could have heard him – at other times – you would know he didn't mean it.'

Jason looked at him, the ebullience gone from his eyes. 'I don't believe you,' he said finally. 'I simply don't believe you.'

* * *

Everything about the cremation service seemed tired. About a dozen people attended. Angelique, who spent the whole service looking like she had something to say, and a male nurse from Foxglove. Anna, of course, and the children, Becky and James, and an old friend of their father's called Bob who had fought with him in the Coldstream Guards and who sat at the back. They sang incongruously, "For Those in Peril on the Sea", and less incongruously, "I vow to thee my country", but their voices would have been unheard had it not been for the rousing CD that backed them. David kept a very close eye on his brother who had volunteered to say something. He chose a quote by Spike Milligan:

"My father had a profound influence on me, he was a lunatic," and then went on to make a generous speech as to why this wasn't the case and how much he owed to Paul. It took him every ounce of grace to do it.

When it came to the eulogy itself, David felt curiously choked. He was furious with his father for what he'd done, which had left a much greater legacy than the ten thousand pounds in cash. It was so utterly misplaced, so completely unfair. It soured everything; the otherwise unblemished life diminished for ever by a single act of treachery. He didn't want to think of Paul like that, fumbling in the dark for the scrap of paper that could be used to damage his son. It was not the sort of thing Paul would have done. He told himself, and Jason too, that it was just the bloody dementia that had twisted everything up in his mind but, in the end, he continued to wonder. Could Paul the generous, loving father really have done something so cruel – even in the grip of mistake?

Though he didn't say anything, David feared that it had affected Jason deeply. It wasn't that he was particularly withdrawn, that was not in his brother's nature. But his eyes had a curious "lost" look about them. He was deeply hurt. As the elder brother, David felt monumentally protective of the debonair man with the immaculately ironed shirts.

'Anyway, you need the money more than me,' his brother had said, with just a touch of intended malice as they poured themselves whiskies the night before his return to the States. 'What will you do out of the long list of things you *should* do? Mend the boiler? Put in a new cooker? Buy poor Anna a new coat? That would be a good thing, she looks like she's perpetually freezing.'

'Anna's all right,' said David a little shortly. 'She's cancelled the weekend away with her god-awful boyfriend, so that's something!'

'Don't you mind about the boyfriend – I mean, really?'

'Why should I mind? I don't care, you know.'

'But she still loves you. She must do, otherwise she wouldn't come round here all the time, picking up the pieces the agency leaves behind. She's very good to you, you know. I think you should be nicer to her.'

David didn't reply. 'Could you just pour me another,' he said finally, holding out his glass. 'Leave it, Jase. What goes on behind closed doors really doesn't concern you. Sometimes peoples' private lives are best left like that… private.'

'Whoa! Sorry! Obviously hit a nerve there! No, it's just that in my book, Anna's a good girl. A really good person.'

'A virtuous person,' said David sarcastically.

'Yes, if you like.'

'Which is better, the good act or the virtuous person? Do you know there's a whole school of modern day ethics that says, in the absence of God, we should go back to what's called "Aretaic Ethics". It's a return to the ancients who had no concept of the good or bad action but only the well-behaved man. Virtue Ethics says we should strive to be good people and the wise acts will follow naturally.'

'But sometimes good people do bad things,' said Jason, thinking of his father. 'How many bad acts do you need before a good person becomes a bad one?'

'And which virtues are worth following?' he added, warming to his theme. 'Correct me if I'm wrong, but didn't the Ancient Greeks place quite a lot of store on being good warriors and protecting the city state?'

'Yes, they certainly liked the good citizen. The one who obeyed, which would have left Mandela and Gandhi out in the cold. They hadn't much truck for people who rocked the system – killed poor old Socrates when he did it! But maybe the core virtues remain the same. Even after all these years.'

'And what are those?' said Jason, pouring himself another whisky and topping up his brother's at the same time.

'Courage mostly, and justice. Courage, wisdom, prudence and justice. That would do it for the Ancient Greeks.'

'Not compassion then. Kindness and love and all that?'

'No, they kind of came later. The after-effects of Christianity, when God gets turned into an ideal of Love and crucified on a cross. Funny how they're the things we look out for today. I think they're rather debased.'

'Meaning?' said Jason, reaching again for the decanter. He was quietly determined to get drunk.

'Meaning that without the others — the older virtues — they're kind of nonsense. I mean whoever heard of kindness winning a war.'

'Maybe, but if everyone was truly kind, wars would never get started.'

'Too wishy-washy,' said David, shifting uncomfortably on his padded cushion. 'Too damned soft. No, I think the Greeks got it about right. Courage, wisdom and justice. If Dad had managed to stay true to himself he would have acted by the last two, every bit as much as he did the first.'

'I think I disagree,' said Jason, more to his glass than his brother. 'I think kindness is all there is. I should know. Until now, I never knew what it was like to have things taken away.'

'But its wisdom and courage that are seeing you through,' said his brother. 'You're wise enough to know Dad didn't really mean it, and man enough to take it on the chin and not go sulking, pretending you've got something to cry about.'

Jason stood up and did a curious thing. He knelt in front of his brother and put his arms lightly on his knees.

'What the devil would I have to cry about?' he said, looking as if he might do it anyway. 'Compared to you —

you're the bravest man I know! Maybe your old Aristotle was right after all. Maybe courage is the only thing worth having!'

Outside, a flock of starlings weaved and dived over the cold London streets. The night was falling and the boiler rumbled flatulently. The apartment was suddenly cold.

* * *

What with the funeral arrangements and Jason's stay, two weeks had passed by the time David was able to return to the library and resume his acquaintance with the Greek girl. He found her much as he'd left her. That was the great thing about dealing with the dead. They were always available when one called.

The attendant went through the same ritual of laying the sheets out to make it easier for him to read. He had made a careful translation of five of the six pages so only one lay undiscovered. It really was a bit like opening a treasure box. He had no idea what loveliness lay hidden inside.

He leant forward and pored over the text.

"The white ox, led from the pasture by unfamiliar hands, is sacrificed on the altar, her neck garlanded with flowers. Her hooves are placid until she mounts the well-worn steps; the steps cut into the hillside that leads to the burning pyre. Only then does she tremble, as she catches the glint of the knife. My master says it is the purpose of a knife to cut well, as it is the telos of the oxen to die.

My belly swells and I am garlanded. My mother anoints me with oil. There will be marriage. To which house might I be taken when I have lived so long in my own?"

David breathed out. A long sigh. He realised that he'd been holding his breath for the last few sentences, struggling with the tenses which bounded from past to present to imperfect in a chaotic impulse, so unlike the perfectly structured Greek of a scholar. But what a text! He could forgive the girl the imperfections in her writing for what she had revealed. The enormity of having an ancient text by a female hand, surpassed even the enormity of who that female had turned out to be. It was, quite literally, unheard of. But then, if this really was the second wife of Aristotle, wasn't it likely that she would be literate and moreover that her works would have been preserved? It was an extraordinary find. He wouldn't grow rich by it. A few learned journals would publish but that was not the point. The point was that it wakened his mind.

He manoeuvred his wheelchair over to the man behind the desk and asked that the manuscript be put away as he had finished it for the day. He ordered Diogenes Laertius *The Life of Aristotle* for eleven o'clock the next day, and then he asked the same man if he would be kind enough to ring for a wheelchair accessible cab. There was something he needed to do.

* * *

Angelique sighed as she put through the call. She didn't expect him to answer straight away because whenever she'd called in the past she'd been forced to wait several seconds. But this time she was pleasantly surprised. He answered the phone straight away.

'Hal-lo.'

'Hello der! David? It's Angelique from de nursing home.'

There was a pause as David grappled with the speaker button. 'That's better,' he shouted, 'I can hear you now. Thank you for coming to the service. It was good to see you there.'

'It's a shame not more people attended,' said Angelique, with the beautiful ebb and flow of her accent. 'Your fader deserved better dan dat poor show. He was a lovely man. One of my favourites, even dough he kept us on our toes.'

'Yes, his great escapes! But you managed them very well.'

'We got used to dem, David. We always knew he'd come back and sometimes de danger is less dan de benefit, if you get my meaning. I would have been fired on the spot if my supervisor knew. Health and safety nightmare, I should say!' she laughed, with the infectious laugh of the genuinely mirthful. 'But never mind, darlin'. Dat's not what I'm ringing you for.'

David waited. He had been right then. She had been trying to have a word.

'I wanted to say somethin' dat day when you came wid your brother. But I didn't find the moment. I needed to speak to you on your own – see?'

'If it's about the outstanding bill, I'm sure I can settle it from Dad's estate.'

'No, no, darlin'. Dat's all perfectly fine. No, it's something your fader said to me de night he died. Something he wanted me to say to you.'

'Go on.'

'Well, I was taking in his milky coffee. You know how he liked it that way. It must have been about ten o'clock. All the other patients were asleep by den, but your father was a late night man. Liked to watch the war films on de history channel. Anyway, I took in his drink and he patted the bed and made me sit down. I never minded sitting down. Could have talked wid im for hours.'

'What did he say?' said David.

'Well, dat night he seemed sort of different, sort of serious. Der was none of the usual talk about de war and de bullets and all that. He seemed awfully sober and he said to me, all urgent like he had to get it off his chest, he said, "Tell David that I was wrong. Wrong about his brother. Tell him to ignore the paper. He's my son," he said, "and who am I to say which is the better soldier?"'

David was silent. 'Why didn't you tell me this before?' was all he could finally say.

'I tried to, but I couldn't find the moment, like I said!' Angelique was just the slightest bit indignant. She was telling him now, wasn't she? 'Anyways, I figured you'd have a lifetime to put it all right.'

David pressed the speaker button which disconnected the call and sat back briefly in his chair. He felt a sudden huge urgency like there was no time at all to lose. The world is such a knife-edge when everything is at stake. Jason could be struck down by a yellow cab in the next few minutes, or choke on a fish bone or fall off his motorbike. Or jump out of the window of a seven-floor building because he thought his father hadn't loved him. And now he knew that Paul – the soldier – had somehow fought through the fog of his illness to surface enough to reach him. The lifetime of love had not been cancelled by the last day of an old man's confusion. Everything was still intact and there was no time at all to lose.

He made the call that he had been by the phone to make when Angelique had rung. He had all the details to hand. He had his debit card and the passport numbers and he knew the name of the place they were going. It was just a matter of doing it.

* * *

It came to almost exactly the amount of his father's entire legacy; the four flights, two from Heathrow and two from New York, plus the hired Mexican carer to spare Anna the effort. He wanted this to be as much for her as him.

'You're mad,' she had said. 'What about the boiler?'

'Sod the boiler,' he replied. 'We might all be dead tomorrow.'

'What about moderation, your old Greek's golden mean?'

'Sometimes it's right to live foolishly if the overall path is wise.'

'Lord, you're beginning to sound like a Greek yourself!'

'Then gather me my chiton, maiden and seat yourself in the grove!' They were still laughing as David managed to reach out and touch her arm.

'Out of the two of us, it dawned on me that you are the really virtuous one in all this. You, and Jason too. I reap all the sympathy and I'm not saying I don't deserve it, but it's not so hard to be well behaved when there's nothing else you could do. Whereas you had choice and yet you chose to stay – in one way or another. That's pretty virtuous in my book.'

'Rubbish!' said Anna, striding in to the kitchen to put on the kettle. 'That's not virtuous. It's what anyone would have done. Besides, there are plenty of people who are ill, who don't see the point in being "well-behaved" as you put it. They rail and scream at their lot, and I can't say I blame them one bit. It's just whatever gets you through, isn't it?'

'Yes. But maybe it makes it easier for others if you're prepared to distance yourself. It's only a body after all!'

Anna looked at him in wonder. 'I don't know how you can say that,' she said finally. 'It's all any of us have got.'

Chrissie was even more glamorous than either David or Anna had remembered. With endless legs that just kept on going until they met her fabulously pert backside, clad in denim shorts. She wore an open cargo shirt that looked like she'd wandered off the set of *Out of Africa* and her blonde hair bounced with effortless life. Jason, too, was tanned and raw with health. Anna felt herself frumpy until David paid for her to have a makeover in the top parlour in La Paz. She emerged looking slim and young again. She'd forgotten what it was to feel that; with the sun beating down on her shoulders.

They hired a large converted jeep and anchored the wheelchair into the back so David could see where he was going and headed up country, stopping for beers on the way at sprawling taverns that appeared out of nowhere, and looked like their owners had deserted them the last time John Wayne passed through. Miraculously, someone always appeared in time to serve chilled Buds which went straight to the back of the throat.

David had had a quiet word with Jason as soon as they were alone that first evening. He found his brother unwilling to talk. It seemed he had shut down on the experience and wasn't keen to awaken its access.

'It's what she said,' he explained, as Jason skimmed a pebble irascibly across the courtyard.

'Yeah, it's just I'm not sure how to take it! I mean I'm not sure a single flash of lucidity is enough to cancel it out. How do we know which was his right mind? How do we know that what he said to Angelique wasn't the dementia and he really meant what he'd said all along – for three years running.'

'Well, we don't,' said David. 'Not for sure anyway. But when you place it in the context of his life, I mean how incongruous was all that? Paul was devoted to you. Remember how he always turned up to watch you play rugby, even when it was pissing with rain!'

Jason nodded.

'Or how proud he was when you got your first break in the City? He was beside himself with pride. It was after, when I first went progressive, that things got bleak for him. And that's when the confusion started.'

'Yeah, well, I guess we'll never know. But I have a stark choice to make. Either I continue to be hurt...and effectively...lose my father, or I take a gamble, believe Angelique and in doing so regain him. It's not a hard call in the end!'

When they got to the San Ignacio Lagoon, they hired a local panga and a father and son crew who looked more than a little askance when they saw the wheelchair, and went off into high-pitched Spanish which translated roughly as "impossible", "too dangerous" and "capsize."

'Tell them I'll sign something,' said David to Chrissie who was doing a good job of negotiating. 'Tell them I haven't come all this way to be put off by a bit of paper. I'll sign whatever it takes to waive them of all responsibility, and then let's bloody well go.'

They had to wear life jackets and David had an extra buoyancy aid round his legs. 'Just in case,' explained Chrissie apologetically. Then, the four men carried him into the boat and sat him up front on the deck. They started the outboard motor and sailed beyond the lagoon.

They didn't hear them at first. They saw dolphins in the distance leaping in the spray, but they were a good way off, and the afternoon was filled with the sound of the outboard and the waves smacking into the side of the craft. Then one of the men gave a shout and there, not fifty yards away, was a spume of water jetting into the air. It was followed by another, and then shortly after the sea parted and a gargantuan creature leapt into the air, smacking back down with a splash like an exploding landmine. The grey whales had arrived. It was impossible to describe their impact. Monsters of the deep who were just passing by, but who stopped off to say hello. It was difficult to know who was inspecting who, as a creature surfaced just yards from the boat. Its enormous dorsal fin carved through the water like a massive oilskin sail.

The whale was as inquisitive as Pandora, whom the gods had made that way and who, after she'd opened her box, left the humans with only hope to live by.

'It's Pandora,' called David, as the others braced themselves, taut with excitement. The whale eyed them with one unblinking eye. Her skin, calloused as rough stone, had white patches that could have been crustaceans or limpets. She disappeared, only to reappear seconds later on the other side of the craft, swimming on her right side, her great mouth open to take in the rich sea life.

'It wants us to stroke it,' called Anna, jumping up in the craft 'Can we? Is it safe?' She reached down into the water and paddled the foam with her bare arm, the water glistening.

The older of the Mexicans nodded. 'She asks for it!'

David was quiet. Something was happening.

Other whales had appeared but this whale was just feet away. The entire boat could have fitted into her body, and if they had all stood on one another they would not have reached the top of her head. She was almost unimaginably big; it was audacious to be that enormous, sustained by tonnes of nothing more significant than plankton. The whale swam close, just feet away from the boat, on the side where David was sitting. The thing that he thought was happening, happened again. David looked into the dark fathom of her eye and saw intelligence there. Deep, restrained intelligence in a creature whose ancestors had been swimming around the globe for millions of years before human history was born. The more he looked, the more he became convinced that she was looking at him, studying him, calling. And then something happened. Her great eye closed and she blinked, and he saw his father in the depth of her eye, connecting as he had when he was well and knew what his gesture conveyed.

The others in the boat were wild; shrieking with joy, dancing and hugging each other, made more abandoned and euphoric than any of them had thought possible by the mere presence of these enormous creatures. But their attention had turned to the other side of the boat where another huge presence was lying as close to them as possible, inviting them to scratch him. David was engrossed with Pandora.

'What do you want?' he whispered. The whale closed her eye again.

'What do you want?'

He felt it in his neck at first; a faint synaptic link that sent a tingle down his arm. Then another, as a stream of energy shot into his hand, with a stab of pain that left him tingling. He looked at his hand, then gingerly, and hardly daring to try, stretched and closed the clawed fist. He opened it again. It was freeing! Sensation was flooding back and it was connected to him again. He could move and control it at will. Like ice thawing, the arm quivered into life until finally it responded as instantly and effortlessly as it had when he was fully well.

The whale's eye never left him. She was encouraging; willing him on.

He leant forward out of the boat and stretched the good arm out, tears pouring down his face, as the great head manoeuvred itself directly under his hand and waited for him to reach her.

'David?' He realised that the rest of the boat had fallen silent, standing awestruck at the miracle that had taken place. Nobody told him to be careful, or not lean out too far. They were just standing in silent astonishment, witnessing the marvel as David laughed and cried, and ran his one working hand over the ancient head whose eye was still watching him, giving him access to another world.

The whales stayed with them for an hour or more putting on a spectacular display, leaping in the air, circling, even gently nudging the boat with their noses. They shared in the euphoria as intensely as the people, and the humans quickly learned that communication is richer and more complex than mere speech and that, at certain times, it soars through the barrier of species as if there were no barrier there at all. When the panga returned to the shore that evening, the numbness crept back into David's arm, but nothing could quell his exaltation. Even as an older man, lying totally paralysed years after the incident had happened, David could not account for the sudden, all too brief, healing. The doctors shrugged their heads and said that MS often followed unpredictable patterns and that a spontaneous remission – albeit temporary – was unusual, while still being normal.

But David knew it was more than that. He had seen the whale's eye, and for a few brief moments gained access to another world. It was the world where his father was, it was the world where the slave girl was. Where nothing is known but wisdom, and the courage to be oneself. It was the world of the great escape, where potential becomes fulfilment and where excellence is lifted above the common herd. It was the world of virtue, and happiness derived from expecting the best of yourself, of becoming what you alone are capable of being, and practicing a life lived well.

* * * * * * * *

The Sage Train was now fully upon them, and the philosopher and the journalist crouched behind their gorse bush like a couple gripped by fear. They could hear the Sages' voices, harmonious and at ease, politely debating and weighing things up. They were all so civilised and evolved. Even Aristippus had found his way among them, complete with a flagon of wine which he drank from frequently, taking comfort in having it there. He was in conversation with Epicurus and debating whether a rose tree was more pleasurable than a rose. Mr Mill looked like he could have settled the matter but was walking with Jeremy Bentham, and was so engrossed that he couldn't stop for the Ancients. It was no matter, there was plenty of time.

Chesterton and Nietzsche looked at each other. They spoke in hushed voices so as not to be overheard. The book in Chesterton's hand, stiffened and lay still.

'That's it. The end of our journey!' It was the Philosopher who spoke first and there was regret in his voice.

'And quite a journey it was!' said Chesterton more blithely than he felt. 'And, after all, we are back up the mountain and at the very place where we began. One more sandwich for the road?'

They munched contentedly in the warm summer sun. The wind was back and was in playful mood, wafting their faces as they ate. They talked about the Sages and flipped through the book, while just yards away the Sage Train wound its way continuously. It was growing, as more and more people joined it; women as well as men and many Orientals.

'It does look fascinating,' said Nietzsche eventually, brushing the crumbs from his enormous moustache and peering through the spikes of the gorse bush. 'They all seem to be having such fun. As if they've found where they wanted to be.'

'Go on then!' said Chesterton. He nursed the book on his knee.

'I'm sorry?'

'Go on then, I said. Join them! You've every right to be there.'

'Me?' said Nietzsche, sweat appearing instantly on his brow. 'Me? On the Sage Train?'

'Why not?' said Chesterton, chuckling. 'Of course you've a right to be there.'

'But I'm mad!' whispered Nietzsche. 'They all know that. I'm mad! Quite, quite mad!'

'Then you're getting less mad,' was the answer. 'You weren't mad when you threw your arms around the horse. You weren't mad when you constructed a new kind of morality. It was just the way you saw it. Don't you think it's the same for all these Sages? Their philosophy was just the way they saw it.'

'I don't know,' breathed Nietzsche. 'I've not thought of it like that. They were all much more brilliant than me, however much I pretended otherwise. I was full of puff and show. My arrogance was all pretence. To hide that I was fearful and small.'

'Go on,' encouraged Chesterton. 'They won't bite you, you know! And here,' he held out the thin volume, with its dirty, moth eaten cover. 'Take this!'

Nietzsche gazed at the volume, back again at the Sage Train and back again at the book.

'*Nein!*' he said. 'My friend! You must keep it!'

'Nonsense,' said Chesterton staggering to his feet. 'You have much more use of it than me. Besides – you're probably in it! I think it wants to go home.'

The German grabbed it then, smiled and raised his head timidly above the gorse bush. Almost immediately a clamour broke out.

'Herr Nietzsche! Professor! How good to see you. We were wondering how long you'd stay hiding. Do you think we can't see you crouched down there? Whether it was your misleading language or a gorse bush; you were always trying to hide. But you're out in the open at last! And you've brought us our book! Please! Do come and join us.' A group of philosophers in the middle of the Sage Train parted to let Nietzsche take his place. He looked overwhelmed and excited, like a child that has just been accepted and finds he has nothing to fear. The book he held in his hand.

'I'm on the Sage Train,' he confided to his nearest companion who just happened to be John Stuart Mill. 'I'm so sorry for calling you a vulgar blockhead,' he added hastily, as a precautionary measure.

'Think nothing of it,' said Mill magnanimously. 'But you do see my point. Your happiness counts quite as much as any of ours.'

'Yes, I do see that now,' said Nietzsche, thinking of the boy and the horse, 'Though happiness counts less than courage.'

Chesterton watched them leave, winding up the mountain as involved and simultaneously carefree as ever. And now both the book and the professor were among them. Good! He was glad he had facilitated that.

'I'm coming! I hear you! I'm coming!' he called to the wind that hid his God from his sight. And slowly, and laughing at nothing, he continued his way down the path.

Bibliography

I am indebted to the books that form the landscape to these stories. In particular I would like to mention

Philosophy and Living Ralph Blumenau Imprint; Academic 2002

The Puzzle of Ethics Peter Vardy and Paul Grosch; Fount 1994

The Puzzle of God Peter Vardy; Flame 1990, expanded and revised published by Fount 1995

A Short History of Ethics Alasdair MacIntyre; Routledge, Rev Ed 2002

After Virtue – a Study in Moral Theory Alasdair MacIntyre, University of Notre Dame Press 3rd Rev Ed 2007

Language Truth and Logic A J Ayer; Dover Publications Inc 2nd Ed 2002

The Story of Philosophy Brian Magee; DK Books PB Reissue 2010

A Companion to Ethics Peter Singer; Wiley-Blackwell New Ed 1993

Practical Ethics Peter Singer; Cambridge University Press 3rd Ed 2011

Ethical Studies Robert A Bowie; Nelson Thornes 2nd Ed 200

The History of God Karen Armstrong; Vintage 1999

The Philosopher and the Wolf Mark Rowlands; Granta 2009

St Thomas Aquinas G K Chesterton; Angelico Press 2011

Thus Spoke Zarathustra Friedrich Nietzsche; Penguin Classics Reprint Ed 1974

Ethics Spinoza (Everyman Paperback Classics); New Ed 1996

On Liberty and Other Essays John Stuart Mill; Oxford World Classics 2008

John Stuart Mill: Victorian Firebrand Richard Reeves; Atlantic Books 2008

Utilitarianism: For and Against J J C Smart; Bernard Williams, CUP 1993

The Cyrenaics Handbook; Aristippus of Cyrene Ed Frank Redmond; Menin Web and Print Publishing 2012

Kant: A Very Short Introduction Roger Scruton, Oxford Paperbacks New Ed ed 2001

Spinoza: A Very Short Introduction Roger Scruton; Oxford Paperbacks Rev Ed ed 2002

Various internet articles especially Stanford Encyclopedia of Philosophy

For further details about the lives and theories of the philosophers, and for information about using The Sage Train with students, please visit my website www.thesagetrain.com

CPSIA information can be obtained
at www.ICGtesting.com
Printed in the USA
BVOW06s1114271217
503781BV00015B/225/P

9 781784 623463